AGAINST THE TIDE

AGAINST THE TIDE

The Story of Adomnán of Iona

Warren Bardsley

WILD GOOSE PUBLICATIONS

www.ionabooks.com

First published 2006 by
Wild Goose Publications,
4th Floor, Savoy House, 140 Sauchiehall St, Glasgow G2 3DH, UK.
Wild Goose Publications is the publishing division of the Iona Community.
Scottish Charity No. SCO03794. Limited Company Reg. No. SCO96243.
www.ionabooks.com

ISBN 1-905010-24-9
13-digit ISBN: 978-1-905010-24-0

The publishers gratefully acknowledge the support of the Drummond Trust,
3 Pitt Terrace, Stirling FK8 2EY in producing this book.

Cover design © Wild Goose Publications
Cover photograph © Jon Crosby

Overseas distribution:
Australia: Willow Connection Pty Ltd, Unit 4A, 3-9 Kenneth Road,
Manly Vale, NSW 2093
New Zealand: Pleroma, Higginson Street, Otane 4170, Central Hawkes Bay
Canada: Novalis/Bayard Publishing & Distribution, 10 Lower Spadina Ave.,
Suite 400, Toronto, Ontario M5V 2Z2

Permission to reproduce any part of this work in Australia or New Zealand
should be sought from Willow Connection.

Printed by Bell & Bain, Thornliebank, Glasgow

To my late wife, Joan, who loved Iona,
and Tom O'Loughlin, who introduced me to Adomnán

CONTENTS

INTRODUCTION

Since beginning work on an MA degree in Celtic Christianity at the University of Wales, Lampeter, I have become increasingly fascinated by the figure of Adomnán (pronounced 'Adovnaun'). The more I have learned about him, the more he has grown in stature. Hence, my puzzlement that so few people, outside of the academic world of medieval Irish studies, seem to know much about him. The fact that he is Columba's (Columcille's) biographer is well-known by those familiar with the story of Iona, of course, but beyond that?

Soon after completing my degree, I presented a paper on Adomnán's *Law of the Innocents* to my local theological society. The group is well-informed and includes a number of Church historians. To my surprise the law was not only news to them, but only one of those present had even heard of Adomnán! Yet, here is a man who ranks among the leading scholar-theologians of the seventh century; someone who not only produced a standard work of reference on the holy places of Palestine and a biography of Columba, but achieved the 'promulgation' of a revolutionary law, the first of its kind, which sought to protect women and non-combatants in time of war.

Adomnán was, by the standards of any period, an outstanding ecclesiastical statesman and Christian humanitarian.

I discovered that though much has been written about Adomnán by scholars, it has been written mainly, if not exclusively, for an academic audience. Apart from Richard Sharpe's excellent introduction in his translation of Adomnán's *Vita S. Columbae*, little or nothing has been published for a general readership. It is because I believe that Adomnán's story deserves to be more widely known that I have written this book.

This book is a work of 'faction'. The word 'faction' may create the impression of a story that contains more fiction than fact. I have tried to be faithful to the *known* historical facts of Adomnán's life (which are sparse enough) and what may reasonably be inferred from them. Some readers will inevitably disagree with my conclusions. For example, I have placed Adomnán in Durrow during the twenty-odd years prior to his becoming Abbot of Iona. There is no textual evidence for this, apart from references in the *Vita S. Columbae* which seem to indicate detailed knowledge of the monastery at Durrow. As far as Adomnán's dispute with his community on Iona is concerned, the major reference to this is in Bede's *Ecclesiastical History of England* (HE V15,V21), where Bede states that Adomnán returned to Iona following his visit to Aldfrith in 689 but failed to persuade his brothers to adopt the Roman rite. My conviction that Adomnán spent considerable periods of time in Ireland between 691 and 697 does have some support in the Irish annals, though the evidence is far from conclusive. However, *if* Adomnán was at odds with his community over the Easter question, his prolonged absence during those years seems perfectly feasible. A more persuasive argument for his absence, in my view, relates to the need to gain widespread support in Ireland for his proposed *Law of the Innocents*. This could hardly have been achieved from a distance. To have enlisted the assent of almost a hundred kings and leading clerics from Ireland and beyond, as 'guarantors' of his Law, must have taken years.

At the end of each chapter, I have included a reflection in which I try to point up the significant historical background against which Adomnán lived his life and, where relevant, some implications for present-day faith and practice. Occasionally, I have included a *table talk* in which I try to imagine the possible reactions of Adomnán's fellow community members to his life and career. Scholars never tire of reminding us (in the words of L.P. Hartley) that 'the past is a foreign country', and of course they are right to do so. Nevertheless, it is a country that, with sensitivity, care and imagination, may be visited. After all, we are of the same flesh and blood as our forebears, and our humanity is the common thread woven into the fabric of our shared history.

I felt a strong impulse to write this book. It is my conviction that Adomnán's life and witness have important things to say to us today. My hope and prayer is that you will discover this to be true and will be as inspired and challenged by the story of 'Adomnán, the illustrious' as I have been.

ACKNOWLEDGEMENTS

I would like to thank a number of people who have made important contributions to this book. First, thank you to my tutors in the Department of Theology and Religious Studies at the University of Wales, Lampeter – in particular, Drs Jonathan Wooding and Tom O'Loughlin, who excited my curiosity and inspired my exploration into the fascinating field of Celtic Christianity. I hope they will recognise their influences, even if they disagree with some of my conclusions!

I am indebted to the Revd Irene Morrow, Dr Margaret Hogan and Mr Jim Houlihan of Birr, County Offaly, who were responsible for organising a conference to mark the 1300th anniversary of the promulgation of the *Law of the Innocents* in 1997. They not only gave me hospitality when I visited the town, but supplied me with much useful local information and actively encouraged me to press on with the writing of this book.

I am deeply grateful to Dr Richard Sharpe, Professor of Diplomatic in the Faculty of Modern History at Oxford University, who took time to go through the manuscript with a fine-tooth comb and saved me from a number of major and minor errors. Of course it goes without saying that I take full responsibility for the position I have taken on the life and career of Adomnán.

The Iona Community continues to be a major focus for my spirituality and is a constant source of inspiration. It is no exaggeration to say that without that influence this book could not have been written.

Finally, my thanks to the staff at Wild Goose Publications for their encouragement and support.

Warren Bardsley,
September 23, 2004:
The feast of St Adomnán
and the 1300th anniversary of his death

PROLOGUE

PROLOGUE

Life can only be lived forward, but it can only be understood backwards.
Søren Kierkegaard

One early-summer afternoon in the year 704 on the tiny Hebridean island of Iona, a lone figure stood on a rocky outcrop and looked out across the Atlantic Ocean towards Ireland. He fancied he could see land but he knew it was an illusion, for he was standing near to the spot where Columcille had landed on the eve of Pentecost, 563 with his twelve companions. This was the 'Hill of the Back to Ireland' close to where Columcille's men had beached the *curragh* which had carried them across the sea, before moving inland to establish their monastic settlement. From here they could no longer see their beloved homeland. It was the place of leaving behind; the place of new beginnings.

Now, 140 years on from that momentous arrival, Adomnán, the ninth Abbot of Iona, successor to Columcille and leader of the monastic *familia* which bore his name, reflected on those tumultuous years, and on how much had been achieved. From humble beginnings on this small island, the gospel had spread east across Scotland, south into Britain, and north to the islands beyond Iona. The Columban confederation was the most powerful and influential in Ireland and Scotland and was renowned across Britain and Europe. Moreover, the community on Iona was growing, numbering almost 200 brothers with always more young men wanting to join than they could accommodate. Adomnán should have been a contented man. His own work, especially during the past ten years, had brought much fame to the family of Columcille. Yet he was troubled in spirit. He knew that his community was deeply divided – a division which, despite his best efforts, remained unresolved. Adomnán suddenly felt exhausted. An old man now, he felt the weight of his mortality. What would become of the community? What did the future hold?

A cool wind was getting up, with dark threatening clouds gathering in the west. He shivered and pulled his cloak more tightly around his shoulders. A flock of wild geese passed overhead, with their raucous disturbing cries. As he looked out to sea, his eyes picked out a small fishing boat approaching the island. It battled against the wind and tide as the oarsmen struggled to make landfall. Adomnán sighed deeply. It seemed a parable of his own life.

The sky grew darker as the storm clouds moved closer. He turned and began to walk slowly inland. There was work waiting: concerns of the community to address, administrative chores to be done. It would soon be the time of the evening office. As he walked he found himself reciting words from Psalm 42, which he had sung so often with his brothers:

Why are you cast down, my soul, and why disquieted within me?
I shall wait for God; I shall yet praise him,
My deliverer, my God.

CHAPTER ONE:

A Donegal Childhood

CHAPTER ONE: A DONEGAL CHILDHOOD

I have loved the land of Ireland – I cry for parting;
To sleep at Comgall's, visit Canice; this were pleasant.

Attributed to Columcille, from a ninth-century manuscript

Sometime in the year 627, a boy was born to Rónán mac Tinne and Ronnat of the Cenél Conaill branch of the royal Uí Néill in south-west Donegal. This was the dynasty destined to become the first to claim hegemony over the whole of Ireland – an achievement marked by much bloodshed.

At the time of his baptism the child's parents chose for him the name Adomnán, meaning 'little Adam'. This was an unusual name in seventh-century Ireland and among the family there was not a little questioning about it. Ronnat, a devout Christian and a strong-minded woman, simply replied: 'Adam was the first man and Christ is the second Adam – what better name could we have chosen?' From the beginning she believed in God's special purpose for the child, a purpose linked to the service of humanity. Her conviction was deepened by the words of an old priest who had prophesied at the time of Adomnán's birth that he would become a leader of his people and would bring many to faith. Ronnat's belief in her son's destiny never wavered and he was nurtured by her love and prayers through his growing years.

It was clear from an early age that Adomnán was an outstanding child. Like all boys he had to learn the basic arts of hunting, animal husbandry and warfare, although they held little interest for him. He loved the rhythm of the changing seasons against the background of the spectacular Donegal landscapes, and the Celtic feasts which marked the changes of the year – Samhain, Imbolc, Beltaine and Lammas. These were matched by the great Christian festivals – Advent, Lent, Easter and Pentecost. He thrilled to the lighting of the

Easter fire and the triumphant cry: 'Christ is risen!' Of course, the Christian faith did not affect Irish society to the same extent as pagan beliefs. As one writer put it: 'Christianity triumphed; paganism survived.' Much had been achieved; much remained to be done.

Adomnán loved to walk the Donegal glens and shorelines and reflect on the history of his people. In the evenings he listened, enthralled, to the elders of the tribe as, in the flickering firelight, they recalled the stories of the ancestors and the great warrior heroes, such as Níall of the Nine Hostages. He never tired of hearing the story of his most famous kinsman – Columcille – who had turned his back on a military career to become the founder and leader of a great monastic *familia*, centred on the tiny island of Iona. In Adomnán's imagination Columcille was a truly great warrior-hero who had battled with and overcome his inner demons and had fought tirelessly for peace and reconciliation in the name and power of Christ. On the feast day of Columcille, the young Adomnán would thrill to the words of his eulogy written by the poet Dallán Forgaill:

> He suffered briefly until he triumphed:
> He was a terror to the devil,
> to whom the mass was a noose.
> He destroyed his meanness:
> he destroyed the darkness of jealousy …
>
> He fought a long and noble battle against flesh.
> He was learning's pillar in every stronghold.
> He was a full light.
> He was an ample fort for the stranger.
> He was obedient, he was noble,
> his death was dignified.

For as long as he could remember, Adomnán had cherished the ambition to belong to the community founded by Columcille. Of course, there were pressures to go in different directions. He felt the sharp stirrings of adolescence and the attraction of young women. He knew that to embrace the monastic life would mean turning his back on the possibility of marriage and children. Then there were the pressures that came from certain family members.

'He has the makings of a lawyer in him,' was a point of view often expressed, and it disturbed Adomnán.

True, he possessed a mind that was razor-sharp, curious, always searching and probing. Rarely was he on the losing side of an argument. His was an analytical mind, quick to grasp the essentials of an issue. Moreover, he could see the steps needed to turn an idea into reality. There was something of the politician in him. Yet he was anything but cold and detached; like his mother he felt a deep compassion for the poor and the most vulnerable members of society. Although he often sought solitude, he had the capacity for making deep and lasting friendships.

Ronnat was steadfast. She had carefully and prayerfully nurtured the spiritual life of the growing boy. She had taken him to Derry on more than one occasion, where he met the prior and observed the daily life of the community. Now the time of decision had arrived. Ronnat reminded Adomnán of their dreams, and of the prophecy of the old priest at his birth. She urged him to fulfil his destiny. Later, alone in his room, Adomnán pondered his mother's words. They had always been close but he had to be sure in his heart that this step was the will of God. As he prayed, a deep sense of inner peace came over him and he dedicated his life to Christ. When he next made the journey to Derry he did not return home. His training as a monk and priest had begun.

During the next thirty years he was to develop into one of the leading scholar-theologians in Ireland and Britain. He studied the Bible and the

Church Fathers in that great flowering of Irish medieval scholarship. He excelled in Latin studies. It was not a narrow world. Irish scholar-saints like Columbanus were travelling to Europe and establishing communities, and students from Gaul, England and Wales were journeying to Ireland in pursuit of Christian learning, among them Agilbert, a future Bishop of Paris. Both Bede and Aldhelm comment on the strength and vitality of Irish biblical studies. Adomnán's surviving works are eloquent proof that much of his career had been focused on scholarship.

These were turbulent years that would bring great changes in Ireland. Power struggles, inside and outside the Church, sometimes impinged on each other and dominated the latter half of the seventh century. Some of the changes were to affect Adomnán profoundly and to present formidable challenges to him and his community.

REFLECTION

During the 1990s, my wife and I worked for a short period as volunteers with the Iona Community on the isle of Iona. I was an abbey guide and my wife worked as a housekeeper. One of my duties was to show visitors around the Abbey buildings, explaining something of the history of Iona and the work of the present-day Iona Community. On my second day, a party of seventy Austrians arrived, few of whom knew English. In at the deep end with a vengeance! However, with the help of an interpreter, we did the tour, and they seemed appreciative. After their questions, I had one of my own. Why, I wondered, had they come to Iona?

'We have come to discover our Christian roots,' said one of the party, and they all nodded in agreement. They went on to explain that in their home town there were streets named after Columbanus and other Irish saints who had planted the Christian faith in their area. (This was not an isolated instance. One of Hildegard of Bingen's monastic houses was at Disibodenburg, Germany – the site of an earlier community founded by an Irish monk named Disibod.)

We are not always aware of the debt we owe to those sixth- and seventh-century Irish men and women who penetrated as far as the Danube to witness to the gospel and plant communities of learning and caring wherever they went. Professor Michael Richter has powerfully detailed this crucial contribution. He writes: 'It is a sobering thought that a fairly full account of Irishmen abroad, as well as foreigners in Ireland, could not have been written on the basis of Irish sources alone, nor even by drawing predominantly on Irish sources.'[1]

Note:

1. *Ireland and her Neighbours in the Seventh Century*, Michael Richter, Four Courts Press, 1999, p.15

CHAPTER TWO:

Turning Points

CHAPTER TWO: TURNING POINTS

Nation will go to war against nation, kingdom against kingdom; there will be severe earthquakes, famines and plagues in many places ... When all this begins to happen, stand upright and hold your heads high, because your liberation is near.

Luke 21:10–11,28 (REB)

The year 664 was a decisive one in Irish history. In that year, at the Synod of Whitby, the Northumbrian king, Oswiu, had voted for the adoption of the Roman dating of Easter and the wearing of the Roman tonsure for all those in monastic orders within his kingdom. Colman, Bishop of Lindisfarne, had resigned in protest and, after returning to Iona, eventually retired to the isle of Inishboffin, off the west coast of Ireland, with a small group of monks. The Columban communities were left to lick their wounds. But the date was also remembered in Ireland and Britain as the year when plague broke out. The plague came in waves during the rest of the century, bringing famine in its wake and decimating whole communities. The plague and its ramifications had a profound effect on Adomnán and his thinking. He wrestled, like succeeding generations, with questions about the place of natural disasters in a world created and sustained by a God of love. Not surprisingly, he, by and large, followed the accepted wisdom of his time. Whilst affirming that those who were spared should be grateful to God for protection, he stops short of saying that those who suffered death were the victims of some kind of divine punitive action. He certainly attributed his own deliverance and his community's to the grace of God; to the intercession of the saints in general and of Columcille in particular. It is clear from reading the end of Book II of the *Vita S. Columbae* that Adomnán believed in miracles and the power of God to heal. But plague was not the only threat facing the Irish people.

The journey had been difficult. Continuous driving rain had made paths slippery, and streams and rivers were swollen and dangerous. There had been reports, too, of unrest in the area due to local feuding. But the journey had to be made. Adomnán was travelling to Brega with his parents, sisters and brothers to be present at the marriage of a relative. It was just before his entry into the monastery at Derry. On the third day of their journey the rain began to clear and walking became easier. There was much light-hearted banter and at times Adomnán would ease his mother's tiredness by carrying her on his back. They would reach their destination by late afternoon, before darkness fell.

Around midday they were approaching a settlement; Rónan felt that it would be a good place to stop, eat and rest before completing the last leg of their journey. There was a strange brooding silence about the place. Smoke rose above the trees and they were conscious of a sickly smell. The forest opened into a clearing, through which a stream ran. There a horrific sight greeted them. The mutilated bodies of several women and children were strewn across the clearing. On the far bank of the stream was the decapitated body of a young mother. One of her breasts had been cut off and at the other was a baby who could not have been more than a few days old. The shocked silence was broken by a terrible wailing. It came from the depths of Ronnat's very being. She had crossed the stream and was kneeling beside the dead woman. Miraculously, the baby had survived. Ronnat held her close to her own breast.

'We must take her with us,' she said through her grief and tears. There was nothing more they could do. They walked on to Brega in silence.

That night Adomnán found it difficult to sleep. His mind was full of images of the aftermath of the slaughter they had witnessed earlier in the day. What had those people done to deserve such a terrible and violent fate? How could

Ireland be true to Christ and his teaching and tolerate such atrocities? Suddenly, he was aware of his mother standing by his side. There were tears but also a fierce anger in her eyes. She took Adomnán by the shoulders and looked steadily at him. As he met her gaze she said, slowly and deliberately: 'My son, one day you will be a great Christian leader. Promise me, in the name of the Trinity, that you will use your power and influence to end this wanton killing of women and children. Promise me!'

Adomnán had never heard such passion and urgency in his mother's voice. He had no idea how he would fulfil such a far-reaching promise, but without hesitation he whispered, 'Mother, I promise.'

In future whenever Adomnán looked back on that awful day he would recall it as a significant turning point: a moment when, through his mother, God had spoken to him.

Reflection

One of the turning points in the Christian history of the British Isles was the departure of Columba from Ireland in 563 to found a new community on the tiny Hebridean island of Iona. In 561, a major battle was fought between the northern and southern branches of the Uí Néill in which over 3000 perished on the field of conflict. The exact cause of this battle and the part played by Columba, a prince of the northern Uí Néill, is not clear; but there seems little doubt that he was crucially involved. One version of events states that his illegal copying of a psalter was the spark which ignited the flame of war. As a monk, Columba was called to account at a synod held at Tailten and afterwards went into penitential exile, either enforced or voluntary. Like Martin of Tours (c.316–397), Columba turned his back on militarism and became an 'island soldier' fighting a different kind of battle.[1] Twelve years after his arrival on Iona, we find him at the Convention of Drum Cett, called to settle present and future leadership of the two related kingdoms of Dál Riata (North Ireland and Western Scotland). Columba was evidently a leading player at this significant meeting and may well have been the moving spirit behind it. Some historians maintain that the convention secured peace between the two kingdoms for fifty years. It is interesting that one of the major turning points in the life of George MacLeod, founder of the Iona Community, was his experience in the trenches of the First World War, which led to his becoming a passionate advocate of non-violence.

War continues to blight humanity. A recent article in The Independent suggested that the conflict raging in the Darfur region of Sudan could well be the first 'global warming war'.[2] Quoting documented evidence from the International Crisis Group, the article maintained that massive ecological damage has caused scarce resources in Sudan to shrivel over the past forty years. Arab tribes are murdering black Darfurians and clearing them off the land because the region's natural resources are insufficient for everyone.

Reflect for a moment on your own response to situations like this, and on what you can do to make the world a more just and peaceful place. Initially it may be finding out more about a particular conflict situation and its - underlying causes. It may be campaigning for structural change on behalf of those who are most vulnerable, for example in the area of trade or the prolif-eration of arms. It may be learning how as individuals and groups we can act more responsibly to care for God's world. These are urgent concerns.

Notes:

1. An eighth-century Celtic cross dedicated to St Martin stands outside Iona Abbey.

2. 'These small steps on climate change fall short of the drastic solutions we need.' Johann Hari, *The Independent*, September 15, 2004

CHAPTER THREE:

Scholar, Priest and Teacher

CHAPTER THREE: SCHOLAR, PRIEST AND TEACHER

He was a wise and worthy man, excellently grounded in knowledge of the Scriptures.

Bede, on Adomnán, from Ecclesiastical History of the English People

When, therefore, a teacher of the Law has become a learner in the Kingdom of Heaven, he is like a householder who can produce from his store things new and old.

Matthew 13:52 (REB)

It was a bitterly cold morning in mid-January. The first snow of winter lay thick on the ground, with the heavy skies carrying the threat of more to come. The Prior of Durrow sat in the common room, warming himself before a roaring fire as he waited for the bell for midday office. His thoughts were interrupted by the entry of Brendan, teacher of biblical studies, stamping his feet and rubbing his hands against the biting cold.

'You look thoroughly chilled, Brother Brendan. Come and sit by the fire and warm yourself.'

'I'm grateful, Father.'

The prior smiled to himself. He was very fond of Brendan, a man of few words and inclined to be over-ponderous but a good teacher and someone you could rely on in a crisis. The prior had been grateful for his counsel on more than one occasion. He broke the silence between them.

'And how was your class this morning, brother?'

'Good, Father. We have an excellent group of students at the moment. Eager to learn. Very teachable.'

'And Adomnán?' asked the prior.

There was another lengthy pause. Brendan seemed to weigh every word before he spoke, which could be exasperating at times. However, his opinions, when offered, were usually well worth hearing.

'Ah … Adomnán … yes … An outstanding student … Quite exceptional. He poses questions at times, Father, to which, I confess, I have no ready answers. He combines breadth of knowledge with an eye for detail; thorough scholarship and imagination. His Latin is already excellent. And there is nothing arrogant about him. He has a genuine thirst for knowledge. Yes, quite exceptional.'

'So, you predict a bright future for him?' asked the prior.

'Undoubtedly. I can see him in time becoming one of our leading scholars … But there is something else about him which I find attractive. He has a deep feeling for people, and especially for those who are disadvantaged in our society. For instance, the other day I heard that he had taken up the case of a woman whose husband had been treating her brutally over some trifling matter and gained redress for her.'

'Interesting. And how exactly did he manage that?'

'He used the law to secure justice. And isn't that what the law is for?'

The prior nodded in agreement. 'Can you see him, then, as a future leader of our community, brother?'

Another pause. Then Brendan smiled (which was an event). 'Oh yes, Father. He is a natural leader. His brothers relate well to him. And, most importantly, he has a vision for the Church and its role in society.' He paused again, and frowned. 'But my fear is that he would be overwhelmed by the weight of administration. We need his scholarly and theological gifts, Father. They must not be lost!'

The bell was ringing. It was time for the midday office.

Durrow was one of the growing number of Columban monastic houses in Ireland. Founded by Columcille himself, it was strategically situated in the midlands on the border area between the territory of the northern and the southern Uí Néill. Not as large or as famous as its near-neighbour, Clonmacnoise, it had a well-earned reputation as a centre of excellence in the study of the scriptures and had produced some outstanding scholars. It was also famous for its scriptorium, where scribes and artists worked with skill and imagination on beautifully illustrated gospel books.

After his initial training at Derry, Adomnán had come to Durrow to sit at the feet of its renowned teachers and concentrate on his biblical studies. He was in his element. He loved the rhythm of the monastic days – its pattern of work and study permeated by the life of prayer in the communal offices and periods of private meditation. His pursuit of learning was relentless. He spent much time in the monastery's library, poring over texts, translating and interpreting. His great passion was theology – a theology based on sound biblical scholarship and applied to the personal, social and political realities of contemporary Irish society.

In his early days as a monk, Adomnán was ordained priest. He loved to visit the folk in the Durrow countryside, to talk with them and help them with their problems, to preach and celebrate the Eucharist. Often people would come to the monastery for counsel, or to do penance, or for practical assistance. No one was turned away. Soon Adomnán was sharing in the teaching of the many young men who came to offer themselves as candidates for the monastic vocation. One of his students was Aldfrith, the future King of Northumbria. When Brendan died, Adomnán became head of biblical studies. He could not have wished for anything better. He felt fulfilled … and yet occasionally (although he found difficulty in putting his finger on it) there was a feeling deep inside him of a vocation not yet completed ... a voice which refused to be silenced.

Adomnán belonged to a small group of Irish scholars who were keen to develop a theology of Church and society. They met from time to time to exchange ideas and saw their work as part of the vital process by which Ireland could be more fully Christianised. They cherished a vision of society in which secular rulers would be anointed by the Church and know themselves to be answerable to God, and drew on biblical models such as the anointing of Saul and David by the prophet Samuel. They also gave much thought to the questions of the Roman dating of Easter and of how the Christian faith could be linked to Irish secular law. In later years, two of their number, Ruben of Dairinis and Cú Chuimne (a pupil of Adomnán), produced a list of canons which contained some of this thinking. They saw themselves not only as recorders but as *makers* of history.

REFLECTION

Because the Synod of Whitby played such an important part in the story of Adomnán – especially during his years as Abbot of Iona – we should try to appreciate something more of its significance in terms of the history of that time.

Some see the synod as an unqualified disaster: the moment when the Church took a wrong turning. Others regard the triumph of the Roman Easter as inevitable, necessary even, to preserve the unity of the Church. It is important, however, to retain some perspective. In Ireland itself there were monasteries and monastic confederations which had already adopted the Roman dating of Easter and the Roman tonsure. The arguments between the Roman and Irish parties, which became bitter at times, were concerned with much more than the Easter question. As Professor Richard Sharpe has observed: 'In the Irish Church the Romani lost all the arguments except Easter.' Whitby was essentially a Northumbrian Council, and its ruling related specifically to that region. Historian A.P. Smyth maintains: 'The real issues at Whitby were neither Easter nor the tonsure but, rather, the problem of political and ecclesiastical control.'[1]

The decision of the Synod of Whitby did not spell the end of the Celtic Church or its influence, although certainly its repercussions for Iona, and especially for its mission on Lindisfarne begun by the Irish monk Aidan in 635, were profound. The distinctive marks of the Celtic tradition – dedication to learning, the sense of God's presence permeating the natural world and the whole of life, the tension between detachment and engagement, creative imagination, justice for the poor, humility and asceticism – were threatened but not lost. In a sense, Cuthbert, Bishop of Lindisfarne (d.685), became a kind of bridge person between the old and new ways. Although he embraced the Roman rite, he exemplified in his life and leadership the true marks of Celtic spirituality; as Dr Clare Stancliffe observes: 'Cuthbert …

fits convincingly into an Irish mould, which was in turn influenced by Antony and Martin of Tours, whilst not being identical with either.'[2]

Moreover, as Michael Richter points out, Northumbria (apart from a brief period of four years following the synod and up to the death of King Oswiu) was a region in which Christian teachers from all parts of Britain were welcomed and esteemed, well into the early years of the eighth century. The whole of Ireland, also, continued to be a favourite venue for Northumbrian monks looking for Christian learning of any kind. Richter concludes: 'While it is impossible to quantify this Irish presence in Northumbria, it can be confidently said to have been substantial as well as formative.'[3]

In the light of the Synod of Whitby it is relevant to ask questions about the way the Church uses power and is used by it. When is it necessary to compromise in order to preserve something of value? When is confrontation the right stance? And when is it a hindrance to discerning God's will? In what significant ways was Adomnán's use of the growing strength of the Columban communities in the service of his grand project – a law for the protection of women in times of war – a right use of power? A Church which seeks to follow the servant Christ will always have to wrestle with questions of power. It certainly cannot avoid them.

Notes:

1. *Warlords and Holy Men*, A.P. Smyth, Hodder Arnold, 1984, p.125

2. 'St Cuthbert and the Polarity between Pastor and Solitary', *St Cuthbert, his Cult and Community to AD 1200*, Edited by G. Bonner, D. Rollason, C. Stancliffe, Boydell Press, 1987

3. *Ireland and her Neighbours in the Seventh Century*, Michael Richter, Four Courts Press, 1996, p.104

CHAPTER FOUR:
Abbot of Iona

CHAPTER FOUR: ABBOT OF IONA

Who knows whether you have not come to the kingdom for such a time as this?
Esther 4:14 (RSV)

On a spring morning in the year 676, the community at Durrow was preparing to receive an important visitor, due to arrive later that day. Failbe was Abbot of Iona and leader of the monastic *familia* of Columcille, and he was in Ireland on a pastoral visitation of the various Columban communities scattered across the island. Word had reached Durrow that Failbe was in poor health and that his stay would not be a long one. He had also sent a message to the abbot requesting a meeting with Adomnán.

Adomnán was curious. It was not unusual for the leader of the community to set up personal meetings with individual brothers. But why send word in advance? Adomnán sensed that, somehow, this meeting would be different.

Next morning, Adomnán was in his room working on a manuscript when Failbe called. They embraced warmly. Two men who had known each other for many years. Blood relatives and brothers in Christ, there was mutual respect between them. There was a silence; then Failbe spoke:

'My brother, we have been friends for a long time. I think we have an understanding. I will come straight to the point. I am an old man, and I sense that I have not long to live. I am deeply concerned about the future of our community.' He paused.

Adomnán could see how frail the old man was, and the effort required for what he was about to say. He was listening intently now.

Failbe went on: 'In one sense, we are strong. Young men are still wanting to join us in considerable numbers. There are some bright young scholars among them – and you more than anyone else know the importance of that. You have set high standards. The artwork done by our scribes and craftsmen is magnificent – all to the glory of God. But we are in danger of looking inward and resisting change.' Now he looked directly at Adomnán. 'We need someone who possesses both gifts of leadership and a broad vision of the place of our community in these islands and the wider world. I have thought often and prayed much about this matter. I have consulted senior brothers in confidence and I believe that you are the man we need. No one is more respected among us and your reputation outside our community is high. I am asking you to consider becoming my successor as ninth Abbot of Iona.'

Adomnán sat in silence, his mind in turmoil. Normally an articulate man, he struggled to find the right words. 'Father … I am honoured … but this is so unexpected … I am no longer young myself. I had thought to live out my days here in study and teaching. Can you give me some time to think and pray?'

It seemed an inadequate response, but gently and with great understanding the old abbot placed his hand on Adomnán's shoulder and said: 'Of course, my brother. I will return in seven days on my way back to Iona. I must ask you to give me your answer then. Now, let me pray with you.' They knelt together, but there was no peace of mind for Adomnán.

The days passed and the uncertainty in Adomnán's mind intensified. He found it difficult to concentrate on his duties. Even teaching, which usually animated him, was a struggle. Why me? Why now – when so much that he had worked for seemed to be coming to fruition, not only at Durrow but in the sphere of his wider political influence? Was he not needed here in Ireland?

On the evening before Failbe's return he went into church with his brothers as usual for the evening office. As he sat in the darkened sanctuary with light from the candles casting shadows on the walls, he thought of these men with whom he had shared life for over twenty years, to whom he had given and from whom he had received so much. Tears came to his eyes at the thought of leaving them. Words from Psalm 40 swept over him:

I waited and waited for the Lord.
Then I said, 'Lo, I come; in the roll of the book it is written of me.
I delight to do your will, O my God;
your law is within my heart.

In that moment he knew what that 'something more' which had been nagging at him on and off for years was all about. He was a servant of God – called to go wherever the community placed him. He would not simply accept the will of God. He would embrace it, rejoice in it, delight in it! He felt a great burden lifting from him. He was at peace.

Naturally, Failbe was delighted with Adomnán's decision. 'You must arrange to leave Durrow within the next few weeks. It is important that we prepare for a smooth succession.'

That made good sense because, although Adomnán was renowned throughout Britain and Europe, he was not known personally on Iona, having never lived there.

The brothers at Durrow were devastated by the news of his imminent departure. They too would need sensitive pastoral care as they prepared for the changes that were to come. Meanwhile, Adomnán spent time with his *anamchara*, his 'soul friend' (see p.62), and went on retreat to a lonely place: to listen for God and ready himself for the challenges that lay ahead.

Now the moment of parting had come. They had all gathered to say goodbye; the brothers and members of his family were joined by people from the nearby villages. He embraced them all, and received their gifts. Ronnat was there; she was old now and arthritic but her back was straight as she came proudly forward with her gift of wool and asked for her son's blessing. As he held her and blessed her through his tears, he wondered if he would see her again in this life.

'Go with God, my son,' she said, her voice breaking with emotion, 'and remember the promise.'

A large crowd accompanied him and his fellow travellers to the edge of the settlement, some walking a mile along the road until they reached a small hill. Then he turned briefly, waved and was gone.

A strong wind was blowing from the north. Resolutely Adomnán wrapped his cloak around himself and turned his face to the wind. His long journey to Iona had begun.

TABLE TALK (in the dining hall on Iona)

Three brothers, Niall, Fergus and Colum, are deep in conversation. Fergus is rather more senior than the other two.

Colum:	I understand that we are soon to welcome a new brother into our community.
Fergus:	Yes, and no ordinary brother! Adomnán is the finest Latin scholar in Britain, and renowned throughout Europe. He is a brilliant teacher. My brother was one of his students.
Niall:	So, why is he coming here now? We have good scholars and teachers on Iona. And isn't he an old man?
Colum:	Rumour has it –
Fergus:	Ah, you're a great one for the rumours, brother. Listening to rumours will get you into trouble … So what rumour is this?
Colum:	Well … it has come to my ears that when our dear Father Abbot, Failbe, dies Adomnán will be nominated as his successor.
Niall:	I have also heard it rumoured that he is not exactly … er … sound … if you know what I mean, on the … er … *big question.*
Fergus:	*(in exasperation)* Now this is getting out of hand! Please stop talking in riddles, brother, and speak plainly; otherwise I will recommend that you do penance for your idle gossip.

Niall: I mean, brother, the question of the date of the Easter celebration and the tonsure.

Fergus: Ah ... *that* question. Well, we shall have to wait and see. In the meantime, you will be well advised to keep these rumours to yourselves. Now, I must go. I have work to do.

REFLECTION

Adomnán's call to be Abbot of Iona came at a relatively late stage in his career as priest and monk. He was in his early fifties, and living at a time when the average life expectancy was between thirty and forty years of age; he was by the standards of the time already an elderly man. On these grounds alone he would have been justified in feeling that this was a call too far. But God does not seem to have much regard for age in his calling of people to particular tasks. Neither age nor youth is a barrier to God when he comes calling.

Reflect on your own situation: Years ago you may have experienced a call to a particular sphere of service – in the world of education, health, politics, the Church ... Maybe now your life situation has changed, either through redundancy, retirement, bereavement or some other circumstance, and you wonder which direction you should take. God may speak to you through a friend, a recurring need, a TV or radio programme, a chance meeting ... The means are many and varied. But be prepared for surprises! You may find yourself protesting: 'But why this, Lord? And why now? My gifts don't seem to fit what you have in mind. And surely I'm a bit too old/young for that.' Yet the inner voice refuses to be silenced.

There is part of the Methodist Covenant Service which reminds us that: 'Christ has many services to be done. Some are easy, others are difficult. Some bring honour, others bring reproach; some are suitable to our natural inclinations and material interests; others are contrary to both. In some we may please Christ and please ourselves. In others we cannot please Christ except by denying ourselves. Yet the power to do all these things is given to us in Christ who strengthens us.' That is what Adomnán discovered: When God calls, grace is always given.

CHAPTER FIVE:

Life in Community

CHAPTER fIVE: LIfE IN COMMUNITY

Three labours in the day: Prayer, Work and Reading.

Take not of food till thou art hungry. Sleep not, till thou feelest desire. Speak not, except on business.

From The Rule of Columcille

In the year 679 Failbe died, and Adomnán was duly installed as ninth Abbot of Iona. It was three years since his arrival on the island. During that time he had enhanced his reputation among the brothers by the depth of his spirituality, the breadth of his learning, his capacity for hard work and his genuine humility. Moreover, he had begun to suggest small but important changes which would improve the life of the community, not least a rebuilding scheme to help accommodate the increasing number of young men eager to join the novitiate and embrace the monastic life after the pattern of the revered Columcille. We have no clear evidence of the size of the community during the last decades of the seventh century; it is quite possible that Iona could have supported between 150 and 200 brothers during Adomnán's abbacy.

In addition to his duties on Iona, Adomnán was responsible for overseeing the various Columban houses in Ireland and the Western Isles. Even though each monastic community had its own prior, the ultimate authority in matters of policy and organisation rested with Iona, and this, inevitably, involved Adomnán in heavy administrative duties. There was also growing work in Pictland, where Adomnán was to develop a special friendship with Bridei, son of Derile, King of the Picts, whom he visited a number of times.

So, what was life on Iona like during the last quarter of the seventh century? In much of what follows, I am indebted to the description given by Richard

Sharpe in his introduction to his translation of the *Vita S. Columbae*.

Although we know little of the shape and size of the original Columban settlement, we can say with some degree of certainty that it would have stood on the raised beach of cultivable land where the present Abbey stands – facing east, overlooking the Ross of Mull. The only major feature still visible today is the vallum, or boundary bank, which enclosed the monastery. Within this enclosed space there would have been several buildings: the church, with at least one side chapel; the abbot's hut; a large domestic building where most of the monks lived, slept and took meals; a guest house where the many visitors who came and went could stay; a kitchen, separate from the other buildings because of danger from its large fire; a library; a scriptorium for copying manuscripts; and a workshop where craftsmen carved in wood and stone. There would have been a barn where grain was stored and a shed for drying corn. Lastly, there was the burial ground of the monks which, in the Middle Ages, became the final resting place of the kings and princes of Scotland.

It is perhaps stating the obvious that a large community, living on a small island, subject to capricious weather conditions, would need to be highly organised in order to survive. Most of the brothers were engaged in some kind of manual work for part of each day; though, as the settlement expanded, there were those (probably lay brothers not subject to the discipline of the rule) who were set aside to farm and fish – work on which the community depended for milk, meat, wool and leather. Food was not plentiful but was nourishing. The community had its own harbour and built and maintained its own boats. Although the monks were good seamen, sailing could be dangerous. The Irish annals record several instances of brothers being drowned in the sea around Mull and Iona.

The heart of the community was the church; its heartbeat, the life of worship and prayer to which the brothers were summoned by the ringing of a hand bell throughout the day and night. Central to the liturgy was the chanting or reciting of the psalms, which were learned by heart; the entire Psalter was read through during the course of each month. Hymns were sung and the gospel read. The Eucharist was celebrated on Sundays at midday and on feast days when, at the discretion of the abbot, a special meal was served. Fasting was normal on Wednesdays and Fridays. Easter was the great festival of the year.

Reading and study were an important part of the daily routine. Iona had one of the best libraries in Britain and a deserved reputation for its scholarship. Adomnán's arrival would have further enhanced that reputation. In addition to the Bible in Latin, probably the Vulgate, the library would have included apocryphal works; writings of John Cassian and the Church Fathers; Augustine's *City of God*; various biographies, including Sulpicius Severus' *Life of St Martin*; as well as liturgical books, histories and works of canon law.

The scriptorium was where the skilled work of making copies of the Psalter and the gospels was pursued with care and devotion. Here was the cradle of an Irish art form which would reach its full flowering in the eighth century in the magnificent and imaginative work which we know as the *Book of Kells*. Behind the scenes in the scriptorium were those busily preparing the writing materials – the parchment, ink and pigments – on which this art depended.

At any one time, there would have been a number of brothers absent from the settlement: some engaged in preaching and teaching missions in Pictland or the Western Isles; some on silent retreat on Hinba, or some other remote island off the Scottish coast; some, at the discretion of the abbot, on longer pilgrimages. The tradition of seeking a 'desert in the ocean', 'the place of one's resurrection', was seen as a vitally important aspect of the monastic life, although the place of resurrection might as likely be found in the midst of the life of a bustling monastery.

Iona itself was a place of pilgrimage for visitors from the mainland and from further afield, and a place of sanctuary for refugees from wars and local conflicts. Our modern understanding of a monastery as a place cut off from the world is far removed from the life of the early Celtic monasteries, which were deeply involved in the social and political life of the period and in the affairs of the locality. As Ian Bradley has pointed out: 'In scattered rural communities with no other institutions or centres, they often fulfilled the role of hospital, hotel, school, university, arts workshop, night-shelter and drop-in day centre, as well as church, retreat house, mission station and place of prayer and spiritual healing.'[1]

Inevitably, as in all communities, tensions arose from time to time – sometimes over major issues, and sometimes over trivial matters. Although little is known about the 'drop-out rate' among the monks, there would undoubtedly have been those brothers who left the community to return home because they could not live with the rigorous asceticism of the Columban rule. (It should be said, however, that the rule of the community on Iona was not as strict as that of Columbanus, for example, in which unquestioning adherence to the authority of the abbot was invariable. Columban monks could – and did – question the word of the abbot.) Probably the rate of defection among the Columban monks was low because of one major factor: the level of pastoral care practised within the community.

Could there have been time for leisure in such a community? Perhaps not in the way that we understand it; but rest days were observed on Saturdays as well as Sundays. There was a balance and a rhythm to life, and time was certainly given to contemplative silence both in the monastery and out in the open spaces of the island. Creative imagination was given free rein, as Thomas Clancy and Gilbert Márkus have amply evidenced in *Iona: The Earliest Poetry of a Celtic Monastery*.

There is a poem traditionally attributed to Columcille (though almost

certainly composed by another writer; someone who knew and loved Iona
deeply) which reflects the pattern and rich variety of monastic life on the
island during the abbacy of Adomnán. It is also a striking example of the way
in which the Celtic Christians read God in the 'great book' (nature) and in the
'little book' (the Bible):

> That I might bless the Lord
> who orders all;
> Heaven with its countless bright orders,
> Land, strand and flood;
> That I might search in all the books
> That would help my soul;
> At times singing psalms;
> At times contemplating the King of Heaven,
> Chief of the Holy Ones;
> At times at work without compulsion,
> This would be delightful.
> At times plucking duilisc from the rocks,
> At other times fishing;
> At times distributing food to the poor,
> At times in a hermitage.

IN THE COMMON ROOM

Adomnán:	Brothers, we are expecting visitors from northern Britain tomorrow. They are likely to be with us for a week or more. Brother Kevin, is the guesthouse prepared?
Kevin:	Father, we have no problem providing hospitality for those who let us know in advance that they are coming. They normally bring some food with them. It's the casual visitors who turn up and expect us to keep and feed them.
Luigbe:	*(shocked)* But, brother, what are you saying? We have no right to refuse hospitality to anyone who comes to us, regardless of status or prior notification.
Kevin:	That is true, brother, but we do have our own needs to consider. The harvest was not good last year and our grain and corn supplies are low.
Luigbe:	That means we must share what little we have. Remember our Lord's words: 'I was a stranger and you took me in. I was hungry and you fed me.'
Kevin:	And then there is the question of carelessness. Brother Colman is regularly at fault. Yesterday, he was carrying a pail of milk to the kitchen and spilt most of it – then he expected Columcille to perform a miracle and refill it! We really cannot afford such waste.
Colman:	*(contritely)* I am truly sorry. I will try harder. It's just that … I

find my mind wandering and I trip over a stone or something.

Adomnán: Brother Colman, we all admire your capacity to meditate. You just need to remember that there is a time and a place ... Now, I would like to raise an issue which has been troubling me for some time. Several of our community have become ill recently, and even now five brothers are so sick that they can neither work nor worship. It is a type of diarrhoea. I have now traced what I think is the source of this malady. One of our wells has been contaminated. A wild animal must have fallen in and has polluted the water supply. We need to make sure that this well is emptied, that any remains are taken out, and that the well is thoroughly cleaned before it is used again. I have recently written some simple instructions about this sort of thing, soundly based on scripture and good sense, and I intend to have them read out at our next meeting. We cannot expect the Lord to look after our health if we don't take simple precautions. Now, are there other matters?

Aidan: I would like to mention the matter of singing in church, which has deteriorated lately. Too many of us seem to be singing out of tune. I intend to arrange some practice, especially for the new brothers.

Adomnán: Quite right, brother Aidan, but remember that the psalmist enjoins us to make a *joyful* noise to the Lord. There is also the question of arranging soul friends for the new brothers and suitable times for silent retreats. We will deal with those matters at our next meeting.

REFLECTION

The level of pastoral care in any community is of crucial importance. Thomas O'Loughlin has drawn attention to Adomnán's use of legal knowledge in his work as a pastor.[2] He refers to a strange set of regulations known as the *Canones Adomnani*, the majority of which relate to food and health issues. O'Loughlin has no doubt that they are authentic, and that they reflect a genuine attempt by Adomnán to relate Old Testament law to the situations of his day. This was a valuable service in medieval society, which made no clear distinction between 'health regulations' and 'moral rules'. In these canones, Adomnán is offering clear guidance in answer to the real questions which cropped up in his community and beyond. In this he was fulfilling his vocation as a Christian pastor: someone concerned about the health of the *whole* person. Similarly, in the eighteenth century, John Wesley produced a manual called *Primitive Physick* which contained simple remedies for a variety of ailments. We may smile at some of these now but, in an age when poor people had no access to medical help, it was a valuable resource, and shows how Wesley, like Adomnán, sought to care for the bodies as well as the souls of his people.

This holistic approach to pastoral care is also apparent in the Celtic application of the sacrament of penance. Here again, the medical model applies. There is no point in prescribing one *single* remedy for a variety of spiritual ills. The penitential must fit the *particular* disease, otherwise it will not effect a cure. And the process is ongoing. The provision of an *anamchara* (soul friend) for each brother, including the abbot, was a vital part of this ongoing pastoral care. An *anamchara* was a kind of cross between a counsellor, confessor and companion. Linked to the sacrament of penance, it provided a level of pastoral care from which the modern Church could learn much.

Notes:

1. *Colonies of Heaven*, Ian Bradley, Darton, Longman & Todd, 2000, p.11

2. *The Irish Penitentials*, edited by Ludwig Bieler, Dublin Institute for Advanced Studies, 1975, pp.176–181. Quoted in *Celtic Theology*, Thomas O'Loughlin, Continuum, 2000, p.74

CHAPTER SIX:

Holy Places, Holy People

CHAPTER SIX: HOLY PLACES, HOLY PEOPLE

I am the Lord your God; you are to make yourselves holy and keep yourselves holy, because I am holy.

Leviticus 11:44 (REB)

There is no holiness except social holiness.

John Wesley

There was great excitement on Iona. Word had been received of the imminent arrival of Arculf, a bishop from Gaul.[1] Adomnán was especially excited because they were receiving not only a continental church leader but one who had travelled extensively in Palestine. Like all biblical scholars of his day he had a keen interest in the geography and topography of the Holy Land. Augustine had raised the question of apparent contradictions in scripture and had written that a detailed knowledge of the geography of Palestine could resolve some of these questions. Adomnán wanted to provide teachers of scripture throughout the Western Church with materials which would be helpful in their work of expounding the Bible. The visit of Arculf, with his first-hand knowledge of the holy places, would give Adomnán the opportunity he had been seeking for many years to write a standard work of reference.

How long Arculf stayed on Iona is not known but it may well have been several weeks. During that time, we can imagine the two men sitting down together, Adomnán full of questions, taking copious and careful notes; Arculf confirming or contradicting accepted wisdom. Sometimes they talked far into the night; by day they walked around the island, deep in conversation. Some of their work would have been done in the community's library, making particular reference to the writings of Jerome. No doubt they would also have found time for more general discussion about the state of the Church and the phenomenal expansion of the new Middle Eastern religion of Islam.

Some time after Arculf's departure, Adomnán began work on *De Locis Sanctis* (*On the Holy Places*). Written in Latin, it attempts to show how an accurate understanding of geography can resolve some of the apparent contradictions in scripture and is based on the assumption that biblical text is fundamentally reliable. Adomnán hoped that his book would gain a wide circulation and eventually find a place in the library of every monastic house in Britain and Europe. Producing books was a painstaking, skilled and costly enterprise, and production had always to be demand-led. Thomas O'Loughlin writes: 'The text of *De Locis Sanctis* shows Adomnán as a most competent and searching scholar, keenly attuned to textual problems and ingenious in his solutions. It is wholly Adomnán's book, the fruit of many years of study and reflection.'[2]

De Locis Sanctis was written not on a sabbatical but, as the author himself states, 'in the midst of ecclesiastical cares'. These few words provide us with a fascinating and poignant insight into the motivation of a scholar who, in spite of the heavy weight of church administration, was moved to produce an academic work of originality and usefulness.

IN THE KITCHEN

My name is Cormac. I am a brother on Iona and I have been a member of the community for twenty years. I love this island – Columcille's island – though I come from Derry in Ireland. I work in the kitchen preparing food for my brothers. I have to say that I couldn't share all the excitement about the bishop from Gaul. Don't get me wrong. I have a great respect for our abbot. *He's* a holy man all right – as interested in those of us who work in the kitchen as he is in the scribes and artists who work in the scriptorium – and you can't say that about all of them I can tell you! But the time he spent with that bishop! We didn't see him for days on end. All about the holy places. But isn't this a holy place? And aren't my kitchen utensils holy? It seems to me that everything we touch is holy because it all comes from God and belongs to Him. That's what I think anyway. Well, he's gone now – Arculf – so perhaps we can get back to normal.

REFLECTION

What does it mean to describe a particular person as holy? Most people would explain it in terms of some kind of moral purity, and this is certainly an element in the biblical idea of holiness. But it is not the only – or even the most important – element. When we read the Holiness Code in Leviticus, it quickly becomes apparent that holiness is at root about relationships – with people, with the land, with God. Because God is just and compassionate, he requires the same attitudes in his people. Allegiance to God means living in community with justice and compassion. So, to treat a neighbour unjustly is to act in an unholy way. By the same token, to relate to a neighbour justly is to practise holiness. Nor is the word 'neighbour' narrowly defined. Dr Jonathan Sacks, in The Dignity of Difference, has pointed out that in the Hebrew Bible the command to 'love your neighbour' appears only once, but the command to 'love the stranger' occurs no less than thirty-six times! This inevitably brings us into the world of economics and politics.

In the New Testament, Jesus had some hard words for those who equated holiness exclusively with 'ritual cleanliness'. He touched the leper, healed the daughter of a Gentile woman, sat down to eat with 'ritually unclean' people – because he was acting in the name of the just, compassionate God who is the Father of everyone.

What does it mean to describe a particular place as holy? Places are not holy in themselves, except in the sense that every place is hallowed ground. In the Celtic understanding, holiness is ascribed to places because of their association with particular people (saints), who manifested the holiness of God in powerful ways. Their holiness was recognised and affirmed; their lives were an inspiration, and a challenge to holy living. I was reminded of this on a recent visit to Taizé, the international ecumenical community in France founded by Brother Roger after the Second World War. At the end of the evening service, Brother Roger remained in the church as hundreds of (mainly) young people came forward to receive his blessing. Young people are not easily fooled. Here was something authentic. Holiness may be difficult to define but it is instinctively recognised.

Adomnán's deep interest in the holy places of Jerusalem and its environs is linked to the understanding that these are sites at which the great drama of human salvation was played out – in the life, death and resurrection of Jesus Christ. Here God is powerfully active – therefore it is important to have as much accurate and detailed information as possible.

De Locis Sanctis is not a travellers' guide to the Holy Land. It is about the serious business of holy living and holy dying. It begins with a description of the gates of heaven, and ends with a description of the gates of hell. Life is about choice; and Adomnán wanted to underline the importance of that choice and to assist pilgrims on their journey to the New Jerusalem.[3]

Notes:

1. In his Ecclesiastical History of the English People, Bede suggests that Arculf had been shipwrecked on the west coast of Scotland and made his way to Iona. A more credible explanation is that Arculf went deliberately to the island, having planned an extended visit. After all, ample evidence exists that Iona was by this time a remarkable and famous centre of learning.

2. Celtic Theology, Thomas O'Loughlin, Continuum, 2000, pp.80–81

3. Thomas O'Loughlin, op. cit., p.83

CHAPTER SEVEN:

Hostage Crisis

CHAPTER SEVEN: HOSTAGE CRISIS

How could we sing the Lord's song in a foreign land?

Psalm 137:4 (REB)

I huddle insensible as blank air; and fear the vertigo of the night seeing myself dropped, God knows where, from such a height.

Brian Keenan, from An Evil Cradling

The early summer of 685 had been unusually warm and sunny on Iona. The life of the community flourished. The last year's grain harvest had been exceptional; cattle and sheep were generally healthy; levels of milk and wool production were good; and among the brothers there was a pervasive sense of happiness and well-being. At dusk, on an evening in late May of that year, two men knelt in church before the altar. The wind moaned through the roof rafters; the candles flickered, casting shadows on the rough walls. That very afternoon, momentous news had reached the island. Carried by special messenger, it simply said: 'Ecgfrith, King of Saxon Northumbria, has been killed in battle at Nechtansmere. Ecgfrith's family have requested that he be buried on Iona. His men will be arriving with the body tomorrow. They will then escort Aldfrith to Bamburgh to claim the throne.' Now, Adomnán and Aldfrith, abbot and king-to-be, knelt side by side.

Aldfrith, the childless Ecgfrith's half-brother, was the illegitimate son of Oswiu, King of Northumbria, and an Irish princess. Educated for the priesthood, he had spent many years in Ireland as both scholar and teacher before coming to Iona. He had in fact arrived on the island some time before Adomnán. The two men had become firm friends with a mutual respect for each other's gifts and achievements.

Aldfrith spoke, his voice heavy with emotion. 'Father, you know that I have not sought this. God knows that my dearest wish is to stay here with you and my brothers and to end my days on Iona. But I know where my duty lies. I will need much help from God if I am to rule my people well. Now, give me your blessing.'

After Adomnán had prayed with Aldfrith and laid his hands on him, asking for the anointing of God's Spirit, they knelt in silence together for some time. As they rose to leave the church the abbot spoke feelingly:

'We are sorry that you must leave us. I, especially, will miss you. Your friendship and counsel has meant much to me. Be assured that your brothers and I will pray for you each day. It is now, as you know, fifty years since Brother Aidan went from this place to preach the gospel in Saxonia. A strong foundation has been laid. Teach and encourage your people in the way of Christ. You will not fail. God goes with you. I will arrange to visit you soon.'

The day after Ecgfrith's burial, the whole community gathered at the harbour to bid an emotional farewell to Aldfrith; after final prayers he stepped into the *curragh* with his escort and left Iona to keep his date with destiny.

It is more than likely that Adomnán had been party to conversations with northern English Church leaders – notably Cuthbert and Aelffled (Abbess of Whitby and Ecgfrith's sister) – who were anxious to see a Christian king on the Northumbrian throne. Following the example of Columcille, Adomnán proba- bly saw himself in the role of kingmaker. In any event, the crowning of Aldfrith was to herald a period of fruitful cooperation between the Columban *familia* and the Saxon kingdom, which would be to the mutual benefit of Ireland and northern Britain.

One day, later that same year, Adomnán was reading in his hut. One of the younger novices had asked to see him about something that was troubling him. No matter how busy he was, the abbot felt that it was important to set aside time for any member of the community who sought his advice. He knew that this particular brother had found it difficult to settle on Iona, and Adomnán had a shrewd idea of the reason why.

'Ah, Brother Ciarán, come in. It is good to see you. Tell me, how is your family in Brega?'

Ciarán hesitated. He was a little overawed in the presence of the abbot. 'Father … I … it's about them that I have come to speak with you. When I came here my parents were not happy.' He paused, then went on hurriedly, 'Not that they were against my joining the community, you understand; but when King Ecgfrith raided Ireland two of my brothers were taken as hostages to Northumbria. I was the only son left in our family, which is now struggling to make a living. I was wondering, Father, now that Aldfrith has become King of the Saxons,' an earnest pleading came into his voice, 'do you think … I mean … is there a chance that he could be asked to set the hostages free so that they can go home?'

It was a request which was simple and heartfelt.

After the young monk left, with a promise from Adomnán that he would do what he could, Adomnán reflected on what he had heard. He was deeply sympathetic. He, too, had relatives and friends in Brega. He knew something of the shock and outrage felt by the people of that area in the aftermath of Ecgfrith's savage attack. Lives had been lost, and property, including monastic buildings, had been looted and destroyed. There was a smouldering hatred in Brega towards the Saxons which would not take much to ignite. Slowly an idea began to form in his mind, an idea which, if it worked, would lead not only to the release of the hostages but to a healing of the rift between the Irish and the

Saxons. He called for a scribe and dictated a letter to Aldfrith. The visit to his old friend was going to take place a little sooner than he had intended.

It was a motley group of mostly men who gathered in the open space outside the fenced compound that had been their home for the past two years. Their bodies were thin and their faces pinched. They had been virtual slaves, with heavy work and little to eat. They were exhausted and several were ill – yet Adomnán could sense a feeling of hope amongst the group of sixty hostages, who were about to embark on the long journey home to Brega.

Three months earlier, in the spring of 686, Adomnán, in the company of a small group of Iona monks, had made a journey into Northumbria to be guests at the court of his friend, King Aldfrith. It had been a joyful reunion. (Although, since the Synod of Whitby, Iona no longer had jurisdiction in Northumbria, Adomnán regularly visited the community on Lindisfarne, spending some time in conversation and prayer with Cuthbert at his isolated cell on the Inner Farne.) The main reason for this visit to Northumbria, however, was to negotiate the freedom of the Irish hostages. Adomnán had come not only as a friend but as the leader of the monastic *familia* of Colum-cille, whose protection extended over the lands of the Irish in Scottish Dál Riata and Pictland. Supremely, he had come in the name of Christ who, echoing the words of the prophet Isaiah, had announced: 'The Spirit of the Lord is upon me, because the Lord has anointed me to bring good tidings to the afflicted; he has sent me to bind up the broken-hearted, to proclaim release to the captives, to set at liberty those who are oppressed, to proclaim the acceptable year of the Lord' (Luke 4:18–19). This commitment to justice and peace was an essential part of Adomnán's duty as Christ's representative and minister.[1]

With the scriptures before them it had not taken Adomnán long to convince

Aldfrith that it was time to release the Brega hostages. And both men could recognise the political advantages that would follow.

Soon it was time to leave for Brega. In addition to supplies of food, Aldfrith had arranged for a detail of soldiers to accompany Adomnán and the hostages to the coast, where boats would be waiting to carry them back to Ireland. He had tried to dissuade Adomnán from travelling with the party himself, pointing out the possible dangers of such a journey, but Adomnán was insistent. It was his duty. Moreover, they'd be far more likely to reach the west coast in one piece with him in charge!

All the same, as he addressed the group, Adomnán could not suppress a twinge of doubt: 'My friends, this is not going to be an easy journey. The terrain in parts is rough and we could well meet with hostile forces. All of you are weak and some of you are ill. We will have to travel slowly – and we do not intend to leave anyone behind. But God is with us … and we are going home!'

A cheer rose from the freed hostages. Then Adomnán led them in prayer, commending them and their journey to God.

They travelled the road running from Berwick-upon-Tweed down to Hadrian's Wall, following the line of the wall towards Carlisle. This was all part of Aldfrith's kingdom. The pace was even slower than Adomnán had imagined it would be. They needed to rest frequently and some of those who were sick had to be carried from time to time. Inevitably there were those who said they would have been better off back in Bamburgh, but generally the spirit was positive with the stronger folk taking the trouble to help the weaker ones. Adomnán was tireless, moving along the line, encouraging, rebuking when necessary, and ministering to the sick. They walked by day and rested at night, sleeping in sheltered areas. Some villages they passed through were unfriendly and on one occasion, when they were met by a band of marauding brigands, they were grateful for the protection of Aldfrith's soldiers. A journey which would normally have taken between two and three days extended into weeks – but eventually they came in sight of the sea, and made their way down the Solway Firth to Whithorn, the place of Ninian and the church dedicated to St Martin. Here they received generous hospitality before taking the short crossing by boat to Bangor.

At Bangor, they were received by the brothers at the monastery founded by Comgall from where the great Columbanus had embarked on his mission to continental Europe. Then, it was on foot again, down through the eastern region of Ireland where the generous hospitality of the monastic houses refreshed them as they neared their journey's end. News of their imminent arrival had reached Brega and a huge crowd waited to welcome them. There were emotional reunions and celebrations far into the night.

Adomnán needed to rest before travelling again on his pastoral round of the Columban houses. It was not just the physical effects of the journey on a body which was no longer young that had exhausted him, but the mental and emotional strain of caring for the hostages over a period of several weeks. He was thankful that, apart from one elderly, dying man who had insisted on travelling, everyone had arrived safely. He spent some time in Brega. One day, when visiting his relatives, he was introduced to a shy woman in her early thirties. 'This is Ronnat,' they said. 'She is the baby your mother rescued from the battlefield many years ago. She is now married with children of her own. We named her after your mother.' His mother had been dead for some years but looking at Ronnat induced a sharp stab of memory. And he recalled the promise – especially the promise.

REFLECTION

In the 1990s, the autobiographies of Terry Waite, Brian Keenan and John McCarthy helped many people to appreciate, for the first time, something of what it feels like to be kidnapped and held prisoner in a foreign land. More recently, there have been disturbing pictures from Iraq of terrified hostages being threatened with death by gun or sword, unless certain demands are met. Often the only 'crime' these people have committed is to have been in the wrong place at the wrong time. Their fate is out of their hands, and there is a sense of almost total helplessness. The situation in Iraq reminds us that hostages are often used as bargaining counters in war zones, and run the gauntlet of conflicting emotions whilst negotiations proceed for their release. If they are held for any length of time – especially in solitary confinement – longings for home, accompanied by periods of severe depression, become unbearably intense.

Although we recognise the names of a few well-known hostages, there are thousands for whom this reality is a daily experience. Groups like Amnesty International campaign tirelessly on their behalf, and enable us to join in those campaigns by letter writing (to prisoners and to governments) or by more actively working for their release. Terry Waite, in his autobiography, Taken on Trust, tells how a postcard of a picture of John Bunyan in his cell in Bedford gaol and a message which simply said: 'We are thinking of you' helped to save his sanity during a dark period of captivity in Lebanon.[2]

The writer of the letter to the Hebrews calls us to 'remember those in prison as if you were there with them' (13:3) – not an easy thing to do but an important place to begin. We must remember, too, those who, like Adomnán, enter into dangerous places to set the captives free.

Notes:

1. *Celtic Theology*, Thomas O'Loughlin, Continuum, 2000, pp.72–74

2. *Taken on Trust*, Terry Waite, Coronet Books, Hodder & Stoughton, 1993, pp.326–327

CHAPTER EIGHT:

A Brave Decision

CHAPTER EIGHT: A BRAVE DECISION

… although he was their lawfully constituted head, he was unable to persuade the monks of Iona to adopt a better rule of life. Had his authority been sufficiently great he would surely have taken care to correct the tonsure also.

Bede, from Ecclesiastical History of the English People

*A*domnán returned to Iona from Ireland in the latter part of the year 686, his reputation as a church leader and statesman greatly enhanced. It was not only his skill in negotiating the release of the hostages which had brought him acclaim, but his insistence on walking alongside them on the long journey home. He was not, however, without his critics. There was a group of (mainly) older brothers on Iona who felt that the abbot was spending too much time away from the island and was moving beyond the boundaries indicated by his office. They were an influential minority and Adomnán took note of their concerns, without necessarily agreeing with them. Failbe's last words to him before he died had underlined the urgent necessity of leadership which would ensure that the community remained true to the vision and ideals of Columcille. One of the great achievements of the founder-saint had been to bridge the gap between ecclesiastical and secular interests, an achievement which Adomnán was determined to build on and carry forward. He knew how easy it was for movements to harden and lose their inner dynamic.

Apart from his busy life as abbot, two projects now preoccupied Adomnán: the completion of his book on the holy places and a biography of Columcille, to be completed by 697 in time for the centenary of the saint's death. Under the pressure of persistent requests from the brothers, he had begun to gather material for what would be the 'definitive' life story of the founder. Already, similar biographies of Patrick, Brigid and Columbanus had either been written or were in preparation.

By 688, *De Locis Sanctis* was completed. Aldfrith had been urging Adomnán to plan another visit to Northumbria; and when he set out in the late summer of 688, he carried copies of the book for presentation to the king and to the community on Lindisfarne.

Aldfrith, a scholar himself, understood the significance of Adomnán's book. He arranged a special gathering at the royal court in Bamburgh, to which chiefs and clergy from the whole of his kingdom were invited. After addressing the meeting and answering questions, Adomnán presented a copy of *De Locis Sanctis* to Aldfrith. Aldfrith, in turn, presented gifts to Adomnán for the community on Iona, and spoke warmly of the abbot's life and ministry and of their long-standing friendship. At the end of the gathering, during the informal conversation which followed, three monks approached Adomnán. They were from the monastery at Wearmouth; one of them was the Abbot Ceolfrid, who said that they would value a private audience with him before his return to Iona. A date was fixed for Wearmouth for the following week.

Adomnán assumed that Ceolfrid was interested in further detailed discussion of his book, so he carried his own copy when he arrived for the meeting. He noticed that the same two brothers who had been with Ceolfrid at Bamburgh were present. They said little but their brooding presence made Adomnán feel uneasy. They sat down and, after simple refreshments, Ceolfrid came to the point:

'Brother, thank you for coming today. You are undoubtedly a man chosen by God. Your great learning, wisdom and humility are plain for all to see. So, it is a source of perplexity to us – sorrow even – that you and your community continue to practise differently with regard to the date of Easter and the tonsure. This – in spite of the decision of the synod, numerous entreaties by Rome and her representatives, and the conversion of more and more communities in your own native Ireland to the Roman way. We are begging you to consider your position in this most important matter, for the sake of the unity of God's Church.'

Adomnán was taken off guard. He was sure that Aldfrith was not behind this move. The matters raised by Ceolfrid were, he knew, of minor importance to the king, although because of his position he had felt obliged to adopt the Roman rite. He was aware that the two brothers were staring at him, cold expressions on their faces.

Adomnán spoke gently: 'I am grateful to you, brother, for your concern. None, I believe, who know me doubt my zeal for Christ and the well-being and unity of his Church. All the communities which owe allegiance to the Rule of Columcille are, in spite of the differences you mention, loyal to the Universal Church. Some think these matters important. Others,' he paused for effect, 'are not so convinced.'

'Ah brother, but it is how your position is *perceived* which matters,' retorted Ceolfrid. His tone of voice was quiet but determined.

'There is some truth in your words, Brother Ceolfrid. I will make this a matter for serious thought and prayer.'

As he left Wearmouth, and over the next few days, Adomnán reflected on this strange meeting. He knew that sooner or later Iona would have to adopt the Roman rite with regard to Easter and the tonsure, although resistance to change was deeply entrenched. But time could not be reversed. His conviction that change would need to be embraced had deepened during his work on *De Locis Sanctis*. But there was another reason. Following the death of Cuthbert in 687, Wilfrid had become Bishop of Lindisfarne for a year. During that time he had stirred up so much strife that several of the brothers there chose to leave the community rather than expose themselves to physical danger. Realising the pressure Rome could also bring to bear on the Pictish Church, Adomnán was fearful that the continued isolation of Iona might eventually place the brothers in some kind of peril. His conversation with Ceolfrid and his monks had served to strengthen this feeling and acted as a catalyst for the course of action which he knew he must now take. It would be difficult. Just *how* difficult he was soon to find out.

The boat rounded the northern coast of Mull and prepared to enter the Sound of Iona.

Adomnán's companions noticed how preoccupied he had been during the journey. He was lost in thought, only speaking when absolutely necessary. They respected his silence, knowing that there was something important on his mind. For days Adomnán had been turning the question over and over. How should he tackle this issue? What kind of strategy should he adopt? Should he talk to individuals and try to persuade them first – especially those from whom he might expect the most opposition? Or should he take the risk of bringing the issue out in the open at a general meeting of the brothers?

He knew that any course of action carried its own dangers. He consulted his *anamchara,* and listened for God. In the end, he decided that to tackle the issue head-on was the least divisive and dangerous strategy. A few days after his return, he called a meeting of the whole community.

It did not seem unusual to the brothers that their abbot had called them together soon after his return. After all, he had been away for some time – and they were eager to hear news of Aldfrith and the work on Lindisfarne. He began in a light-hearted vein, telling stories of his journey and highlights of his visit to Aldfrith's court. He presented the gifts which the king had sent to the community. Then he paused and cleared his throat. As he looked over the sea of faces – these men who were his brothers, for whom he not only bore responsibility but held deep affection – he drew back momentarily. Then, after a silent prayer for strength, he went on.

He spoke of the past years, reminding them of the Synod of Whitby, and of the heartache that had followed in its wake: the harsh words spoken, the bitterness between brothers, the breaking of ties. That was twenty-five years ago. The time had come to move on; to heal the hurts, find a place for forgiveness and seek, above all, the unity of Christ's body. He spoke with passion and persuasiveness:

'My brothers, I have thought and prayed much over this matter and I believe that the time has come to change – not out of disloyalty to our great founder and Father, Columcille, but in order that his community, to which we are privileged to belong, may be faithful to his vision for this time. I fear that refusal to take this step could well place us in some danger in the future. I implore you to consider this carefully and follow my lead, which I am fully persuaded is God's will … We will meet again soon to make our decision.'

There was a long silence. The atmosphere in the meeting had changed completely. Adomnán could feel the confusion and growing hostility. Then, one of the senior brothers rose to speak. There was anger in his voice:

'Father, let me ask you a question. Were you present at Whitby? Did you witness the humiliation visited on us? Did you feel the shame? Did you see the contempt displayed towards us by Wilfrid and his henchmen? As long as I live, I will never accept this imposition. It is the wrong direction.'

There were murmurs of assent. Others spoke, and the word 'betrayal' was used more than once. All the pent-up feelings harboured over the years came spilling out. Adomnán knew that there were those who supported his proposal. He looked around the meeting, but no one would catch his eye. They had been silenced by the strength of feeling expressed by the opponents of change. One by one the brothers filed silently out of the meeting.

Adomnán felt isolated. He had been shocked by the strength and depth of the opposition to his proposal and the hostility expressed towards him by a number of the senior brothers. Always to some extent an outsider in their eyes, he was now about to be cast in the role of betrayer of the community, its traditions and Columcille himself. He comforted himself with the thought that at least the matter was now out in the open. But he had crossed the Rubicon. He knew that things would never be the same again.

REFLECTION

Bede's Ecclesiastical History of the English People is regarded (rightly) as a major contribution to the story of the Church in the British Isles. It is important to remember, however, that Bede was writing for a predominantly Saxon audience and that, therefore, his work reflects a certain bias. Bede obviously held Adomnán in high regard and included extracts from De Locis Sanctis in his History. However, he tells us that, having failed to convince his community on Iona to adopt the date of the Roman Easter, Adomnán went to Ireland in order to 'correct the ancient error, restoring nearly all who were not under the jurisdiction of Iona to Catholic unity' – but then returned to Iona, made another failed attempt to persuade his brethren, and died the following year, a disappointed man.[1] Whilst there is some truth in this version of events, it ignores what is, unquestionably, Adomnán's greatest achievement, of which we would know nothing if Bede was our only source of information. Also, curiously, Bede has little to say about Aldfrith, the Christian scholar-king who ruled Northumbria for almost twenty years. Could the reason be partly due to the fact that Aldfrith was Iona-trained?

Another point which needs to be made is that the recording of bare historical events reveals nothing of the feelings experienced by those who were caught up them. In the case of Adomnán, we can imagine the effect of the persistent opposition coming from his own community on his physical and mental health. We have no way of knowing for certain because he doesn't tell us, but my guess is that the effect would have been considerable.

Note:

1. *Ecclesiastical History of the English People*, Bede, Penguin, 1955, p.294

CHAPTER NINE:

Gethsemane

CHAPTER NINE: GETHSEMANE

Tired
And lonely,
So tired
The heart aches,
Meltwater trickles
Down the rocks,
The fingers are numb,
The knees tremble,
It is now,
now, that you must not give in …

Weep
If you can,
Weep,
But do not complain.
The way chose you –
And you must be thankful.

Dag Hammarskjöld, from Markings

The weeks and months which followed were the most difficult Adomnán had ever faced. On the surface, little seemed to have changed in the pattern of life on Iona. The rhythm of prayer, work and study continued – indeed how could it be otherwise? Were not these dedicated men: Milites Christi, island soldiers, whose very reason for being was to wage constant spiritual warfare in the name of Christ against the forces of evil within themselves and in the world around them? There could be no respite from that vital struggle.

Yet, although the casual visitor would not have noticed, there were tensions beneath the outward normality. Those brothers who loved their abbot became increasingly concerned for his welfare. Although he continued to carry out his duties with his usual care and efficiency, they were aware of the immense strain under which he was living. He seemed withdrawn, taking long walks daily round the island. He was available less often for private conversation. Those who were most fiercely opposed to him maintained only as much contact as was necessary. Some deliberately went out of their way to avoid him.

Adomnán knew that he was presiding over a community which had effectively turned against him. He found it difficult to concentrate on his work and his mind wandered during communal prayers. He took no delight in his studies or his teaching. He slept little and was constantly tired. Winter seemed to close in more quickly than usual that year. The darkness of the days mirrored the gloom and depression of his spirit. One night, after evening prayers, Adomnán remained alone in the dimly lit church. A single candle burned on the altar, illuminating the large cross on the wall behind. As he knelt, he tried to focus his mind on the suffering of the Lord. At one point, deserted by his friends, he had felt abandoned even by God. The darkness in Adomnán's mind and spirit grew deeper – it was as if he were under attack from all sides. At times, he had struggled hard with the temptation to resent his opponents. The questions tormented him: Had he done the right thing, confronting his brothers so aggressively? Had he been in too much of a hurry? And, if so, was not this proof of his pride? Was it right to have alienated those who had trusted him? A lover of unity, how could he have become the cause of so much disunity? Had he been right to come to Iona in the first place? Tears coursed down his cheeks and he found himself praying: 'Lord … please … I cannot go on … Take this cup from me.'

He felt tiredness seeping through him. He drifted into a state between sleep and wakefulness. Suddenly, he became aware of a light around the altar which seemed to emanate from the cross and from a presence at once disturbing and reassuring. He was conscious of being addressed: 'Adomnán, the time has come to keep the promise.' The promise? Which promise? The promise made to his mother those long years ago? But now? In this wilderness? How could it be possible? The voice came again even more urgently, this time containing a note of command. 'Now is the time. You must travel to Ireland to keep the promise.' It seemed as if his mother and Columcille were beside him, laying their hands on his head in blessing. Suddenly, he was fully awake. Perspiration was pouring from him in spite of the cold. He glanced around. Had it been a dream? Or a vision? He could not be sure. But he did not doubt that God had spoken to him. He found himself praying, 'Father, not my will but Yours be done.' Gradually confusion gave way to assurance. He knew what he must do. Rising from his knees, he walked slowly to his hut and slept as he had not done for weeks.

The next morning, following prayers, he called the brothers together. He announced that he would soon be leaving for Ireland on pastoral visitation and to fulfil a long-standing promise. He made arrangements for the administration of the community, appointing Connamail as deputy in his absence. Though he did not know it then, it would be years before he would return to Iona. Nor did he realise that his greatest achievement was still ahead of him.

TABLE TALK

Niall: Well, brothers, what do you make of all this? Our Father Abbot is leaving us again – and by the sound of things he could be away for a long time.

Colum: I must say I thought he looked better today than he has for ages … As if a burden had been lifted from him.

Niall: But what was all that about a promise? I don't know what to think. Perhaps he's running away. Things haven't been the same since his announcement about the Easter question.

Fergus: Well, you could be right. Look at it this way: It may be better for him to go now so that a new abbot can be appointed to sort out the confusion.

Colum: All well and good – except aren't you forgetting one thing, brother? Abbots have a tendency to go on until they die!

Ciarán: I can't believe what I'm hearing! How can you talk like this? Adomnán is the greatest leader our community has had since our blessed founder Columcille. Who can match Adomnán in his wisdom and scholarship, his zeal for justice and love for the brothers? I tell you, he will be sorely missed.

Fergus: Well, we may not agree with you on all those points, Brother Ciarán, but I'm sure we can all agree on one thing: We must continue to pray for the safety and well-being of our abbot, and for Brother Connamail as he takes up his heavy responsibilities.

REFLECTION: ADOMNÁN THE OUTSIDER

In a sense, Adomnán had always been an outsider on Iona, for two main reasons. First, as we have already noted, he was in his fifties when he came to live on the island and there is no indication that he had been there before, even as a visitor, although we cannot rule out that possibility.

Second, and perhaps more crucially, his appointment ended the arrangement which had lasted for almost eighty years – by which one branch of the Cenél Conaill, the descendants of Columcille's uncle, Ninnid, son of Fergus, had dominated the abbacy of Iona.[1] Adomnán did not belong to this branch of the family but was of the line of another uncle of Columcille, Sétna, son of Fergus. Although this group had never held the abbacy, they were pre-eminent in another respect, for they had been the ruling dynasty of the Cenél Conaill since the late sixth century. It is perfectly feasible that some of the older brothers, who had served on Iona for many years, would have resented the appointment of someone who, in spite of his royal connections, had no direct link with their community and had been 'foisted' on them. There may even have been those who entertained some expectation of assuming the leadership themselves when Failbe died; if that were the case, Adomnán could have been the object of considerable jealousy and resentment. This would probably have contributed to the tensions which arose over the abbot's adoption of the Roman Easter and his attempts to persuade the community to follow his lead.

Whether Adomnán regarded himself as an outsider is of course another question. He was obviously a strong character who was determined to lead; but the impression persists of a genuinely humble man who did not court controversy or confrontation for its own sake. He was probably pushed to the limits over the Easter issue but nowhere does he appear to harbour bitterness or attempt to score points at the expense of those who opposed him. The Vita S. Columbae contains only one neutral reference to the controversy.

It is worth reflecting here on the cost involved when a leader feels compelled to go out on a limb in the cause of progress, even though he knows he cannot take all the members of his community with him, and, in the process, may create temporary discord in pursuit of a greater unity.

Note:

1. *Iona, Kells and Derry*, Maire Herbert, Oxford University Press, 1988, pp.47–48

CHAPTER TEN:

A Revolutionary Law

CHAPTER TEN: A REVOLUTIONARY LAW

To Adomnán of Iona, whose troop is radiant, noble Jesus has granted the lasting freedom of the women of the Gaels.

From Martyrology of Oengus, c 830

Light a candle, don't just curse the darkness.

Chinese saying

When Adomnán arrived in Ireland in the early 690s, the signs for the success of his project were not propitious. There was rivalry between the major monastic confederations, all of whom were courting the patronage of the powerful Uí Néill, now gaining a position of dominance throughout Ireland. A warlike, militaristic culture prevailed and only tiny sparks were needed to ignite full-scale conflict. Meanwhile, successive waves of sickness caused by plague continued to ravage the population. Adomnán had devised an ambitious plan to introduce a new law designed to protect women in time of war, for which he planned to enlist the support of all the kings of Ireland, Scotland and northern Britain, as well as the leading bishops and heads of churches and monastic communities. His aim was nothing less than nationwide agreement for the backing of a law which would be effective and enforceable. In the coming months and years, with incredible singleness of purpose and indefatigable energy, he would marshal all his considerable legal and political skills to bring his master plan to fruition. It was a massive undertaking.

It was vital at the outset to secure the support of the leading kings of Ireland, especially the powerful Uí Néill. Kings were the real movers and shakers of medieval society and Adomnán knew that without *their* backing his project was unlikely to succeed. Accordingly, he arranged to be present at the annual gathering of the Uí Néill kingdoms at the fair of Tailten, held in August. The High King would be present, and Adomnán requested an opportunity to address the assembled court at some point in the proceedings. There was, he felt, something strangely fitting about the place. It was here, in 561, that Columcille had been called to a special synod to answer charges relating to his involvement in the Battle of Culdrevny. From here, Columcille had gone into voluntary exile to begin his great work on Iona.

Adomnán scanned the faces of the men he was about to address; many were familiar to him. Some were his kinsmen. There were warriors present whose exploits on the battlefield were legendary. Adomnán knew how crucial it was to convince these men of the rightness of his project. The High King invited him to speak, introducing him as Abbot of Iona and the leader of the Community of Columcille.

Rising to his feet, Adomnán thanked the High King and the assembly for welcoming him, and conveyed the greetings of his community and the assurance of their constant prayers. He reminded them of Columcille: how he had faced his accusers in this very place; how he had turned his back on the way of military confrontation to become a soldier of Christ, a warrior for peace and reconciliation. It was, he said, in his name that he stood before them. He reminded them of the situation in the country: the loss of life and the decimation of the population through the ravages of war, famine and plague. He mentioned Brega, and the chaos left behind in the wake of Ecgfrith's raid. He paused, then went on:

'My Lords, I am here today to plead for the women of this land who are slain wantonly in battle, whose blood stains our fields and turns our rivers red … Women who are the bearers of life, mothers of our children, made in the image of Mary, the mother of our Lord. I am here to fulfil a promise made to my own mother many years ago in the presence of the blessed Trinity. Today I am proposing a new law to protect the women of our kingdoms in time of war.'

'And how, Father,' asked the High King, 'do you propose to enforce this law?'

'By the imposition of an honour-price set at twice its present value, sire,' replied Adomnán.

The stupefied silence which greeted this statement was broken by gasps of incredulity, and then everyone seemed to be talking at once.

Adomnán could feel a growing hostility, emanating mainly from the warriors in the assembly.

The High King called for order. When he had regained his composure, he said, 'And why double the honour-price, Father Abbot?'

'Because, sire,' replied Adomnán, 'if it were less, the law would be disregarded.'

The assembly was in an uproar now. Adomnán decided to play his trump card. When order had been restored once again, he went on: 'Sire, this law, if passed, would mean a substantial increase in your own power. Once it is accepted across the land by all the kingdoms, bishops and abbots, *you* would have the authority to promulgate the law. This would enable you to protect your people, and could also bring certain material advantages.'

Scepticism began to give way to interest as Adomnán expanded his argument. The right to promulgate and enforce would mark a notable increase in royal power and he knew that no secular ruler would ever be indifferent to that.

The High King was thoughtful. The Uí Néill was indeed seeking a consolidation of its power base across the whole of Ireland – this law could be one useful means to that end. He also knew that Adomnán represented the most influential monastic confederation in Ireland, founded by one of his most illustrious kinsmen. It would be important to be on the right side.

'When do you propose to bring this law into effect?'

'It will take some time, sire. There is much consultation to be done. However, once you have given your support I am confident of success.'

'You must give me some time to consult with my advisors,' said the king. 'But you will have our answer tomorrow.'

Adomnán passed a sleepless night. He prayed fervently that the High King would pledge his support. He must not fail at the first hurdle.

The next day, as the High King prepared to speak, the abbot felt apprehensive. He believed most of his kinsmen would back the proposed law, but the influential warrior class and the unpredictable druids could still put obstacles in the way. He waited with bated breath.

'Father Adomnán, we have given much thought to your proposal. We are willing to support your law on the condition that you succeed in persuading the other kingdoms to do the same.'

Adomnán could barely conceal his elation.

'Sire, I thank you and your council for this promise of support. You have made a wise decision. Now that I have your backing I will spare no effort ... Aldfrith, King of the Saxons, and Bridei son of Bili, King of Pictland, have already indicated their agreement. I will keep you informed of my progress.' He left the assembly after offering prayer and a blessing. The next day he was gone – to continue the work of advocating his project. He had a feeling that the tide was beginning to turn.

Soon afterwards, Adomnán convened a gathering of leading clerics at Durrow, together with some representatives of the legal class. Heads of the two other leading monastic federations, Armagh, the see of Patrick, and Kildare, the centre of Brigid's community, were present, as well as bishops and abbots from all parts of the country. The conference began with two days of prayer and fasting. It was at this meeting that Adomnán's extensive knowledge of Irish law was invaluable. He knew that there were those who would want to get into arguments about detail. Adomnán was determined to secure broad agreement for the larger picture at this stage. The minutiae and fine-tuning could be worked out later. He stressed the theological and humanitarian basis of his proposed law and the calling of Christ's Church to be a voice for the most vulnerable members of society – as well as stressing the material benefits which would stem from its promulgation. Although the imposed fines would, in the case of this particular law, only benefit the Uí Néill and the Community of Columcille, the law would, undoubtedly, in due course, open the way for the promulgation of similar laws by other monastic communities, with corresponding benefits. Adomnán outlined his proposals for sanctions against those who broke the law. He proposed to invoke the judgement of the saints, both dead and living, against offenders, and to pronounce maledictions and curses, which would expose offenders to a form of public disgrace.

There was a proposal from Armagh to extend the provisions of the law to include the protection of children and clerics and Adomnán agreed to this – on the condition that the law's major emphasis would be the protection of women. Although there were some dissenting voices, Adomnán was able to secure the agreement he required. Gaining the support of the Uí Néill had indeed been vital.

The next eighteen months were spent travelling the length and breadth of Ireland, meeting kings and clerics and canvassing support for his Law. He used all the authority of his position as Abbot of Iona; he encouraged, argued, threatened and cajoled, bringing all his considerable skills as lawmaker, politician and negotiator to his task. Wherever he went he rang his bell, gathering the people together, and calling down the wrath of God on any who opposed his Law. Driving him on was the sense of his God-given mission. There were, of course, setbacks along the way. Powerful vested interests opposed his project and from time to time he was subjected to abuse and the threat of physical violence. But he pressed on relentlessly, all the time working at the framework of the law, its provisions and sanctions. By the summer of 696, he was satisfied that his project now had sufficient support across the country and he made arrangements for its implementation. He returned to Tailten that year to report to the High King. His close kinsman, Loingsech, had recently succeeded to this office and was a strong supporter of the Law. Adomnán put before the assembly his final proposal. A special synod would be convened in the spring of 697 on the plains of Birr, almost exactly one hundred years after the death of Columcille. All those who had agreed to guarantee the passage of the Law would be summoned to attend. It would be called the *Cáin Adomnáin*. Before that time, Adomnán planned to go back to Iona. Although he had made two brief visits to the island, he had effectively been away for four years. There were several reasons for returning to his community, not least of which was to oversee the final drafting of his Law. But there was *one* reason above all others: When, in the following year, he appeared at Birr to proclaim his *Cáin*, he knew that it was essential to arrive not as an individual, but as Abbot of Iona, the leader of the Community of Columcille.

REFLECTION

In time, the Cáin Adomnáin was enshrined in the legal system of Ireland. It was likely drawn up by Iona's legal experts, as large monastic confederations, owning considerable amounts of property, had their own law schools. Its significance may be measured from the Crith Gablach, an Irish law tract, which states that there are four chief laws of Ireland: 'The Law of Patrick, not to slay clerics; the Law of Dáire, not to steal cattle; of Adomnán, not to slay women; of Sunday, not to travel.'

To fully appreciate just how ground-breaking and revolutionary Adomnán's Law was we need to bear in mind two important factors. The first is the status of women under Irish law.

Discussions of 'honour-price' in medieval Irish law tracts are concerned, for the most part, with free males. (Honour-price referred to the penalties imposed under Irish law for particular crimes. The low level of fines imposed for crimes against women indicates their low status in Irish medieval society.) Honour-price was estimated on the basis of property, office, skill or training, and because women's access to all of these areas was extremely limited they had independent legal status only in rare cases. In general, a woman's honour-price was estimated as a fraction, usually one half, of that of her 'head' or legal guardian. Moreover, as Professor Máirín Ní Dhonnchadha has pointed out, 'women seem to have constituted the major part of what slave population there was in early Christian times, although there is some archaeological evidence for male slaves'.[1] As a result, the unit of value most commonly referred to is the 'cumal', the original meaning of which is female slave. Adomnán's Law doubles the penalty for the crime of murder against a woman from seven cumals to fourteen. Máirín Ní Dhonnchadha writes: 'Adomnán's Law enhances the status of women by emphasising their role as life-givers while simultaneously drawing an analogy between them and Mary the mother of God.' The Cáin Adomnáin was the first law of its kind in Ireland to deal specifically with the status of women.

The second factor we need to bear in mind is the culture of battle which permeated Irish society. Warriors were heroes whose exploits were steeped in the blood of their enemies. A cursory reading of the Irish annals will be sufficient to show that warfare was endemic in Irish society, as indeed it was throughout Europe. Kathleen Hughes quotes a typical entry from these secular tales: 'Since I took my spear in my hand, I have never been without slaying a Connachtman every day and plundering by fire every night, and I have never slept without a Connachtman's head beneath my knee.'[2] This is the boast of an Ulster warrior-hero, but by the eighth century large fines awaited a warrior who murdered innocent women, children and clerics in the theatre of war. Hughes goes on to say that, although Adomnán's Law can in no way be construed as a pacifist text, the series of cána (laws), of which the Cáin Adomnáin was the first, may have done much to increase the stability of Irish society and to change its warlike ethic. (The idea of a cáin as a contract binding different parties to peace is well brought out in the Irish law tracts, where we find the frequent bringing together of síth (peace) and cáin, síthcáin, meaning 'peace compact', and cáinchomracc, meaning 'peace-convergence, amity'.)

Of course, this warlike culture could not be changed overnight. What the Law of the Innocents did was to use the existing framework of Irish medieval law – but then to go beyond its provisions to create a new protective shield for those most vulnerable in times of military conflict. It was essentially subversive of the existing order. Seen in these terms it was 'a master-stroke, the repercussions of which were felt throughout Ireland'.[3] Kathleen Hughes calls the Cáin Adomnáin a landmark in Irish ecclesiastical history. It united the country around a strongly humanitarian law. Its uniqueness lay not only in its

> provisions, but in the fact that it was promulgated and designed by a Christian leader (whose primary motivation stemmed from his Christian convictions) for the protection of a group of people whose situation had hitherto received no special attention. Adomnán is a peacemaker in the biblical sense. He is one who creates the conditions for peace.

THE PLOT

Somewhere in the south-west of Ireland around 695–696. A local king is meeting with his Council of Elders.

King:
: Who will rid us of this turbulent priest? I hear that he is gathering much support for his law. Our allies in the north are backing it as well as numerous clerics from all over the country. Think of the implications of his proposal. If we kill or defile women in battle or do them violence the fines will ruin us. This is a threat to our whole culture, our way of life. I don't know how we will control our warriors. Can nothing be done to stop him?

Elder One:
: We could try spreading rumours. Perhaps there is something in Adomnán's past ... Some sexual scandal we can dig up. He seems to have a special regard for women. Maybe he likes them *too* much.

Elder Two:
: I have thought of that also. I have consulted leaders in various places and there is nothing. His integrity is beyond question. He is highly respected throughout the land.

King:	So there is *nothing* we can do to stop him?
Elder Three:	There is a way, my Lord, but it is highly dangerous. I understand that Adomnán intends to travel from Iona to Ireland when the time comes to promulgate his law. I believe that without his presence the project would almost certainly fail. I am sure that an accident could be arranged.
King:	You mean … kill him?
Elder Three:	It would require careful planning, sire, but it is possible.
King:	Well then, let us discuss the details.

Notes:

1. 'Birr and the Law of the Innocents', *Adomnán at Birr*, Máirín Ní Dhonnchadha, Four Courts Press, 2001, p.21

2. *The Church in Early Irish Society*, Kathleen Hughes, Methuen, 1966, p.152

3. *Ireland and her Neighbours in the Seventh Century*, Michael Richter, Four Courts Press, 1999 p.75

CHAPTER ELEVEN:

On the Plains of Birr

CHAPTER ELEVEN: ON THE PLAINS OF BIRR

The Lex Innocentium … is a feat of international diplomacy and should be celebrated alike in Geneva and Helsinki as in Birr.

Thomas Owen Clancy

Adomnán at Birr is a courageous even heroic figure.

Thomas O'Loughlin

Try and make your revolution, go into combat, advance a little, even if it is only a millimetre in the right direction.

Hugo Chavez, President of Venezuela

It was a momentous day. It was a day that would live in the annals of Irish history. It was a day that none of those who were present would ever forget. It was a day of victory for the cause of peace and justice. It was Adomnán's day.

Adomnán's return to Iona in the late summer of 696 had been fraught with tension. He knew that to re-establish his authority as abbot would not be easy, but that it had to be done before he returned to Ireland to convene the Synod of Birr. In just a few months he must mobilise the support of his brothers for the *Law of the Innocents*. In this cause he had a valuable asset. During his years of absence in Ireland, Adomnán had continued work on the *Vita S. Columbae* – the *Life of Saint Columcille*; he had carried the almost completed manuscript from Ireland and would arrange for copies to be made by the scribes on Iona. The community was excited by the news, and Adomnán planned to formally introduce the *Vita* to his brothers just prior to his journey to Birr. It would be ready for circulation by the centenary of the saint's death the following year, a fitting way to celebrate a significant anniversary. Moreover, it would go a long way, Adomnán felt, towards convincing his brothers that, despite their differences, he was utterly loyal to the revered founder and the tradition which bound them together. Although here and there resentments still lingered on, Adomnán was satisfied that, as he prepared to return to Ireland, he had the support of his community.

It was on a fine, cool spring morning in the year 697 that the ninth Abbot of Iona set out on the long journey to Birr. His route would take him by boat via the northern coast of Ireland to Derry, and from there by foot through the hills of the north and down to the midland plains. Thomas O'Loughlin has pictured Adomnán travelling through sunshine, wind and rain with words of the psalms ringing in his ears:

'For he will rescue the needy who appeal for help;
the distressed who have no protector.
He will have pity on the poor and needy
and deliver the needy from death:
He will redeem them from oppression and
violence and their blood will be precious in his eyes' (Psalm 72:12–14)

He recalled, too, the words of the prophets, who became a voice for the voiceless, and the care of his Lord for the poor and disadvantaged. He was moving in the power of the Spirit, an ambassador of Christ.

On his arrival in Derry he was met by a group of brothers from the

Columban community there, who would accompany him on his journey. They were anxious for his safety. Enemies were all around. Reliable rumours of a plot had reached them, and the brothers suggested that they take a slightly longer but safer route to Birr. It was a reminder to Adomnán of the pockets of resistance to his project that still remained and which, even at this eleventh hour, might conspire to undermine it. Although he took the threat to his safety seriously, and agreed with the suggestion of the Derry brothers, he was not afraid. He felt himself encircled by the protecting power of God.

He had planned the time and the place of his synod with meticulous care. 697, as we have already noted, was exactly one hundred years after the death of Columcille. Not only was Birr strategically situated on the borders of several kingdoms and close to a number of important church settlements, it was the monastic foundation of Brendan, a friend of Columcille and his lone defender at the Synod of Tailten. Now, in the spirit of Columcille and Brendan, Birr would become a place of peacemaking and reconciliation. Here would be celebrated true unity – a proclamation of the peace of Christ.

Delegates to the synod had been arriving for several days. They had come from all parts of Ireland and were representative of secular and ecclesiastical interests across the land: kings with their courtiers; abbots representing not only the great monastic confederations of Armagh and Kildare, but the smaller monasteries scattered across the country; bishops and clerics from regional dioceses and churches … In the spring of 697, all roads led to Birr.

On the morning of the synod Adomnán rose early. This was the day for which he had prayed, worked and planned for years. He felt the hand of destiny upon him. Alone in his room he knelt and prayed: 'High King of Heaven, God of the nations, I praise You for bringing me safely to this time and place. Bless our meeting and endeavour this day. Drive back the powers of darkness; frustrate the will of those who oppose Your purpose; strengthen me,

Your unworthy servant, and bring us good success.' At morning prayer, the words of Psalm 46 spoke powerfully to them all:

'The Lord of hosts is with us, the God of Jacob is our fortress …
in every part of the wide world he puts an end to war:
he breaks the bow, he snaps the spear; he burns the shields in the fire.'

A colourful scene greeted Adomnán when he arrived at the large open space close to the monastery of Brendan. As the Abbot of Birr led the assembly in prayer, Adomnán sensed that this was an historic moment. Adomnán rose to speak and rang his bell. His voice was strong and clear; those present that day said that they had never heard a speech so evidently delivered in the power of the Spirit. He seemed incandescent – the fire burning within him.

He reminded the assembly of the purpose of their coming together; then, in measured tones, he outlined the provisions of his Law and its specific purpose. He warned of the dire consequences of breaking it, not because the law was his but because it came from God – the God who acts to protect the weak and vulnerable, and whose judgement is severe on those who oppress the innocent. He reminded them of their pledges, and of the pledges of those not able to be present.

'I come to you today in the name of the triune God and his saints, Mary, Columcille and Brendan. I ask you now to signal your assent, as guarantors of the *Law of the Innocents*.'

One by one they came forward to signify their pledge to uphold the Law. There was a great shout as the *Cáin* was proclaimed, echoing and re-echoing around the assembly. As Adomnán's bell rang out again and again, everyone present knew that a powerful blow had been struck for peace and justice. It was a great moment – a moment for rejoicing and celebration.

Alone in his room that night Adomnán reflected on the events of the day. He was drained but deeply grateful to God. He fancied his mother smiling on him. He had kept the promise made to her so many years ago. He had been faithful to his Lord whose words, 'How blest are the peacemakers', were his constant inspiration. Tomorrow he would make plans to travel to Iona. He must be back with his brothers for the celebration of the centenary of Columcille's death.

REFLECTION: VISION AND STRATEGY

The genius of Adomnán lies in the fact that he not only saw clearly what was needed but also knew the route to be taken in the context of Irish law and culture to make his vision happen. He was successful in securing broad agreement for his Law and for penalties which were severe enough to ensure that it would be observed. Like a great general, he brilliantly marshalled his forces to confront the enemy and win the battle. The guarantor list is of particular interest. It is a most impressive document, reflecting what amounts to a pan-Irish agreement embracing Church and state only thirty years after the Synod of Whitby. This was a massive achievement by any standards. Although Adomnán's cause was undoubtedly strengthened by the accession of his Cenél Conaill kinsman, Loingsech, to the Uí Néill High Kingship in 696, the guarantor list is wide-ranging in scope. It includes not only the kings of the Uí Néill and representatives of both the Armagh and Kildare monastic groupings, but kings and clerics from across Ireland and northern Britain.

Máirin Ní Dhonnchadha, who has made a scholarly study of the guarantor list, has compared names in the list with Irish annal entries of the same period. Fifty-eight of the ninety-one names can be identified from their obituaries in the annals. She concludes: 'It cannot be other than a genuine historical record, contemporary with the promulgation of the Law'.[1] Scholar Michael Enright comments: 'This is the highest point of influence reached by the paruchia Columbae and is our first intimation that one church had gained authority throughout the country'.[2]

It may be argued that national and international relationships are more complex today than they were in seventh-century Britain, and there is some truth in that of course; but visionaries who glimpse the ultimate prize still need to devise strategies to achieve realisable goals on the way to their final objective.

Jubilee 2000, for example, was a brilliant strategy, in the context of a larger vision, to secure agreements to cancel crippling debt owed by heavily indebted poorer countries – a step on the road to a more just and equal world community. A recent report stated that arms sales from Britain now exceed £1 billion; and in an article in The Independent (June 8th, 2004), arms control campaigners protested that the government was still permitting arms exports to states with poor human rights records. In a world where one person dies every minute from armed violence, what strategies now need to be devised to control the proliferation of arms – as essential steps on the road to a demilitarised global society?

Notes:

1. 'The guarantor list of Cáin Adomnáin', Máirín Ní Dhonnchadha *Peritia 1: Journal of the Medieval Academy of Ireland*, 1982, p.179

2. *Iona, Tara and Soissons: The origins of the royal anointing ritual in Francia*, Michael Enright, published by Walter de Gruyter, 1985, p.73

CHAPTER TWELVE:

In the Image of Columcille

CHAPTER TWELVE: IN THE IMAGE OF COLUMCILLE

He was an angel in demeanour, blameless in what he said, godly in what he did, brilliant in intellect, great in counsel. He spent thirty-four years as an island soldier, and could not let even an hour pass without giving himself to praying or reading or writing or some other task ... at the same time he was loving to all people, and his face showed a holy gladness because his heart was full of the joy of the Holy Spirit.

Adomnán, from Life of St Columba

When Adomnán arrived on Iona following the Synod of Birr, preparations for the centenary celebrations were well advanced. In a great Eucharistic act of worship on the anniversary of their founder-saint's death, the monks would rededicate themselves to their present vocation of prayer, work, study and mission.

The brothers were recalling the origins of their community in the coming of Columcille to the island: the rigour and hardships of the early years, the opposition, the kindness of strangers, and the slow but sure growth of the monastic settlement. They were remembering sayings of their founder – words of encouragement, warning and prophecy. And now they had an additional resource – the new *Life of St Columcille*. Each day in the dining hall there were readings from the vivid narratives. Not all of it was new; there had been earlier accounts of the saint's life, some of which were incorporated in the new work and which Adomnán readily acknowledged. But the style and form were essentially different. The brothers were moved by stories of Columcille's trials; thrilled by accounts of his travels, especially to the court of Bridei, King of Pictland; challenged by his miracles of healing and his passion for justice; sometimes reduced to laughter by stories which resonated with their own experiences on the island – and moved to tears by the retelling of his final days and his death in the company of his brothers. In this way the life of the community was refreshed and renewed.

TABLE TALK

Dorbbéne: My hand is tired brothers! All this writing! I am just completing my third copy of Father Adomnán's book. It is a great privilege but very laborious; and in these dark winter days, when we have to work by the light of candles, my eyes hurt as well as my hand.

Kevin: *(sympathetically)* It is indeed a great work, brother. The book is bringing much esteem to our community. We pray God will give strength to your hand and your eyes. I love the story of –

Colum: Yes, brother, we know. You have told us many times. But have you noticed the cleverness of our Father Abbot?

Dorbbéne: What do you mean, brother?

Colum: Well, for instance, the story about the spilling of the ink. I imagine that happens quite often in the scriptorium!

Dorbbéne: Oh no, brother, ink is too precious to waste ... But I do remember one incident some years ago when a rather clumsy scribe upset ink over a manuscript I was working on.

Kevin: Yes, and then there is the story of the girl who came to Columcille for protection and was murdered, and how Columcille's curse brought the murderer to a bad end. Think of the inspiration Father Adomnán must have found in *that* story for the promulgation of his great Law.

Dorbbéne: Ah yes, I see what you mean. It is as though he is reminding us that the problems we face now are very similar to those faced by Columcille in *his* lifetime!

Colum: My point exactly, brother.

REFLECTION

The Vita S. Columbae is widely acknowledged by scholars to be an outstanding example of the genre known as hagiography. It is not biography in the sense that we understand the word; it does not set out to present a chronological account of the saint's life, but presents him, in the context of his time, as an outstanding man of God: someone who performed miracles and whose prophecies concerning the future were demonstrably true. In this regard it must be seen as propaganda for the saint, his cult and his community. Professor of History Dáibhí Ó Cróinín goes as far as to say that, with few exceptions, the lives of the saints are a 'dismal swamp of superstition and perverted Christianity, dreary litanies of misplaced reverence and devotion'.[1] The Vita S. Columbae is one of the exceptions. Adomnán goes to pains to point out that he has carefully researched his sources. Although none of Columcille's contemporaries would have still been alive when he wrote, Adomnán tells us that he set down 'without equivocation what I have learnt by diligent enquiry, either from what I could find already in writing or from what I heard recounted without a trace of doubt by informed and reliable old men'.[2] We know that he used extracts from an earlier work written by Cumméne, seventh Abbot of Iona. Like all biographers, Adomnán had a particular purpose in mind in writing his Life of St Columcille. It was to show that: 'this small island on the edge of the Britannic ocean' was indeed part of Christendom and had earned a reputation that was famous not only in Britain but also in 'the three corners of Spain and Gaul and Italy, beyond the Alps and even Rome itself, the chief of all cities'.[3] And this small island was the home of Columcille, who deserved to take his place among the greatest of God's saints. So, although Adomnán was writing chiefly for his own community when he penned the Vita, he almost certainly had a wider audience in mind.

We might reflect, if we are inclined to be dismissive of this genre, on the fact that any attempt to tell the story of an historic leader is bound to be selective, reflecting to some extent the agenda and priorities of the writer and the constituency which he or she represents. This tendency can be seen, for instance, in the attempts to impose modern concerns about the environment on to sixth- and seventh-century Celtic saints. Their deep sense of the reciprocal relationship between God and his creation is wholly relevant to the environmental debate; at the same time we must be aware that their agendas and mental maps were different from our own.

It is evident that Adomnán saw himself and his community 'in the image of Columcille', and that the inspiration drawn from the witness of the founder enabled them to be more faithful to his vision in their own life together.

Notes:

1. *Early Medieval Ireland*, D.Ó. Cróinín, p.210–11, Longman, 1995

2. *Life of St Columba*, Adomnán, translated by Richard Sharpe, Penguin, 1995, p.105

3. Adomnán, op. cit. p.233

CHAPTER THIRTEEN:

Last Days

CHAPTER THIRTEEN: LAST DAYS

Do not go gentle into that good night; rage, rage against the dying of the light.

Dylan Thomas

A domnán sat alone in a small rocky bay below the monastery, overlooking the Sound of Iona and the dark mountains of Mull beyond. He had come to love Iona, with its changing colours, restless tides.

It was a late September afternoon in the year 704. He was now an old man in his mid-seventies; his constant travels, heavy workload and the strains and stresses of controversy had taken their toll on his health. Although blessed with a robust constitution, he felt increasingly frail; he knew in his bones that he was very close to the end of his life. But he was still writing and translating; he loved to teach the new brothers and play a part in preparing them for the life of prayer and mission. The passion for God's peace and justice which had driven him through the years still burned in his mind and heart. His longing for harmony within the community was as strong and insistent as ever. Deliberately he drew a circle in the sand with his stick, reflecting on his journey of faith and on the encircling, protecting power of God.

His reverie was interrupted by the sound of footsteps behind him. Turning round he saw that it was Lasrén, a senior brother, one of those who had opposed him most bitterly over the Easter question.

'Father Abbot,' he said, a little awkwardly. 'I am sorry to disturb you but may I speak with you for a moment?'

'Of course, my brother. Come and sit beside me. Tell me what is on your heart.'

They sat in silence for some time. Then Lasrén said: 'Father, I wish to beg your forgiveness.'

'What is there to forgive?' asked Adomnán.

'Oh, there is much, Father. I have harboured resentment towards you for years. I have spoken hard and bitter words against you. I know now how wrong my attitude has been.'

'My brother, I freely forgive you, as I forgive all who have wronged me. Just as I hope to be forgiven by anyone I may have hurt. But please do not doubt this: in everything I have done I have sought nothing but the will of God and the highest good of this community.'

With that, Lasrén knelt to receive Adomnán's blessing. Then, together, they walked slowly back to the monastery, the old abbot leaning on the younger man's arm.

Later that day following vespers, alone in his hut, he gave thanks for the earlier conversation on the beach. It had warmed his heart and encouraged him to believe that the old divisions were beginning to heal. As he gazed pensively over the sea he wondered what the future held … He could not have imagined that by the end of the century fierce warriors from the north would swoop down like wolves on a fold, looting, killing and decimating the unprotected monastic communities – that, only a stone's throw from where he had sat earlier in the day, sixty Iona brothers would be massacred, their blood staining the white sand and turning the sea red. He could not have foreseen the subsequent departure of the community from its island base and its relocation to Kells, or the later rebuilding of monastic life on Iona under the Benedictines – and how even that movement would eventually succumb to the tide of history, leaving behind only a ruin of stones. He could not have prophesied the twentieth-century renewal and rebuilding of community under George MacLeod, but he would surely have approved of the marriage of an ancient spirituality to a deep commitment to peace and justice, which marked that new beginning.

All this lay in the future. For now, although there were difficult days ahead, the tide was turning. He felt a sudden deep love for his brothers and a fierce desire for their welfare; tears welled up and ran down his cheeks as he commended each one of them to God by name.

Now he was content. The present and future needs of Columcille's family were in safe hands. Of that he was sure. He reached for the manuscript of St John's Gospel on which he had been working. He could perhaps complete the chapter.

When he did not appear at the night office, two of the brothers were sent to his hut. They found him slumped across the manuscript, the quill with which he had been writing having slipped from his fingers onto the floor. He had died at his desk, a scholar to the end. The brothers noticed that the section of the gospel on which he had been working was chapter thirteen, and that the verse he had reached contained the words: 'A new commandment I give to you. Love one another as I have loved you.' It was a fitting epitaph.

REFLECTION

One of the most moving passages in Adomnán's Vita S. Columbae describes the saint's final day on Iona. Adomnán depicts Columcille telling his brothers of his impending death, and their deep sorrow at this prospect. Columba goes with his faithful servant, Diarmait, to bless the community's wheat barn, expressing his happiness that after his passing there would be sufficient bread for the coming year. After confiding in Diarmait the precise hour of his death, he leaves the barn, blessing an old workhorse who leans on his breast in a gesture of mourning. He then climbs a small hill overlooking the settlement and, raising both hands, blesses the monastery, predicting its increasing influence in secular and spiritual affairs. He then continues his work of copying Psalm 34 and goes to Sabbath vespers. After worship he returns to his lodgings and issues these last commands to his brothers through Diarmait:

'I commend to you, my little children, these my last words: Love one another unfeignedly. Peace. If you keep this course according to the example of the holy fathers, God, who strengthens the good, will help you, and I dwelling with him shall intercede for you. He will supply not only enough for the needs of this present life but also the eternal good things that are prepared as a reward for those who keep the Lord's commandments.'[1]

The narrative concludes with the saint's death, before the altar of the church. We are told that the brothers witnessed angels coming to meet him and that 'the whole church was filled with the sound of sorrowful lamentation'.[2]

It is difficult to avoid the conclusion that, in relating this vivid account in such detail, Adomnán was making a thinly disguised appeal to his brothers to keep among themselves peace and harmony.

Notes:

1. *Life of St Columba*, Adomnán, translated by Richard Sharpe, Penguin, 1995, p.228–229

2. Adomnán, op. cit., p.230

EPILOGUE

€PILOGU€

A domnán's death on Iona in 704 is recorded in the Irish annals without embellishment or comment – an indication, perhaps, that the Iona scribe who made the entry was reflecting something of the ambivalence felt towards the abbot by his community at the time of his passing. Like many great men and women, the magnitude of his achievements was only fully appreciated after he had gone. His recognition as a saint was followed, according to custom, by the removal of his relics to Ireland, where they were carried 'on circuit' whenever his Law was renewed. There are numerous references in the Irish annals to these 'promulgations' during the eighth and ninth centuries as the path charted by Adomnán was followed by other monastic communities. Although one negative result of the increased prosperity of the monasteries was growing conflict between them, we can be fairly confident that the periodic renewal of the *Cáin Adomnáin* resulted in a greater security for those it had been designed to protect.

In these days when the word 'great' is bandied about somewhat loosely, by what yardstick do we measure the greatness of Adomnán? We could cite the breadth and depth of his scholarship, the writing of two books of major importance, his huge ability to relate theology to the pressing social and political issues of his day, his wise statesmanship and wide vision ... But he was, supremely, I believe, a *great human being*. It is difficult from this distance to imagine the sheer force of the pressures which he faced during the final years of his life, as he sought to balance the pastoral and administrative responsibilities of leading a large and growing monastic federation with the task of maintaining and developing relationships with secular and religious leaders. The way in which he was able to transcend the difficulties of his latter years speaks of his spirituality and resilience. It is the sheer humanity of Adomnán which shines through time and time again: his humility, magnanimity, compassion, courage and, above all, his passion for justice. He stands in the great Celtic heroic tradition: a champion of peace, reconciliation and right relationships. If some are inclined to express all this in terms of his obedience to the will of God, I would not demur, but I am reminded of the words of a Swedish pastor to someone who was trying to drive a wedge between the divine will and serving this world: 'Do as God – become human'!

We know little of the ninth Abbot of Iona from his own writings, but at the end of *De Locis Sanctis* he allows us a brief glimpse into his mind and heart. It reveals something of the humility and humanity of Adomnán, 'the illustrious':

I have written down these things in what I admit is a poor style, but I have done so in the face of daily labour coming at me from all sides: the amount of ecclesiastical concerns seems everwhelming. So I wish that you who read of these places not neglect to pray for me, the sinner who wrote this, to Christ, the Judge of all the ages.[1]

Note:

1. Adomnán, *De Locis Sanctis*, edited and translated by Denis Meehan & Ludwig Bieler, Scriptores Latini Hiberniae 3, Dublin, 1958.

APPENDIX A:

Ronnat

RONNAT

The material in chapter two relating to Ronnat is based largely on a tenth-century commentary on the text of the *Law of the Innocents*, which was probably part of a sermon preached whenever the Law was promulgated.[1] It tells, in graphic detail and earthy language, the story of how Adomnán and Ronnat come upon a scene of bloody massacre and how, having been unable to give her milk to a baby who has miraculously survived, Ronnat implores her son to do something. He promptly restores the mother of the baby to life, after which Ronnat tells Adomnán that it is his responsibility to 'free the women of the western world'. When he expresses reluctance, she binds him with a chain and places him in a chest of stone until he becomes willing to carry out her wishes and to enact the *Law of the Innocents*.

The story as it stands is somewhat bizarre and scarcely credible. However, it may well be based on oral tradition – which lost nothing in the retelling! Having worked with preliterate societies in Africa I know just how persistent oral tradition is. I was frequently amazed at the accuracy of the remembering, especially when land disputes were involved. What I believe we have here is the memory of an actual incident from the life of Adomnán which, for the sake of dramatic effect, was written up for later generations. What would have been the point of inventing it? It hardly shows Adomnán in a favourable light! It does, however, reveal Ronnat as a formidable woman who was not averse to nagging her son – refusing to give up her struggle for protection and justice for the women of Ireland. That she had a profound influence on Adomnán I have no doubt, and it is this perception that I have tried to develop in this book.

Note:

1. Gilbert Márkus, *Cáin Adomnáin (Adomnán's Law), a seventh-century law for the protection of non-combatants*, translated with an introduction by Gilbert Márkus, Blackfriars Books, Glasgow, 1997, p.4

APPENDIX B:

Adomnán and
the Justice and Peace Commitment
of the Iona Community

ADOMNÁN AND THE JUSTICE AND PEACE COMMITMENT OF THE IONA COMMUNITY

This is an edited version of a paper written by Kathy Galloway, leader of the Iona Community, for the 13th Centenary Commemoration Conference on Iona, 23–27th September, 2004. The conference marked the 1300th anniversary of the death of Adomnán.

Another kind of celebration

September 23, 2004 is being marked on Iona by a special conference at which leading medieval scholars will present papers relating to Adomnán's life and career. It was marked yesterday in Edinburgh by a number of people processing from the east end of Princes Street to Parliament Square, site of both the national cathedral, St Giles, and the Scottish law courts. There they took part in an act of worship – a liturgy commemorating Adomnán's life and the promulgation of the *Cáin Adomnáin*, the *Law of the Innocents*. After worship, the group processed on down to the newly completed Scottish parliament buildings and repeated the liturgy there. As they processed, they handed out leaflets explaining what they were doing and, during worship, rang out the Iona Community's replica of Adomnán's bell, which was gifted to us by the Corrymeela Community, with whom we have close links.

It is fitting that the gift of Adomnán's bell should have come from Corrymeela, a Northern Irish community, both Catholic and Protestant, with centres in Belfast and on the North Antrim coast, which exists to promote peacemaking and reconciliation across communities in Northern Ireland. For it is the theme of peacemaking which connects the Iona Community and the Corrymeela Community, and which links the Iona Community most closely with Adomnán; and of course Adomnán himself is representative of the strong links between Iona and Ireland.

The people who celebrated Adomnán's anniversary in Edinburgh yesterday came from two groups: the Adomnán of Iona Affinity Group and Women in Black.

The Adomnán of Iona Affinity Group is made up mostly of members of the Iona Community who are affiliated with the Trident Ploughshares Movement. Trident Ploughshares campaigns against Trident nuclear-armed submarines across the world; the Adomnán of Iona Affinity Group is particularly concerned with the presence of Trident in Scotland. Affinity groups consist of people (a dozen to twenty) who commit themselves to supporting one another in non-violent direct action against Trident, for which they undertake a period of training. Such action may vary from letter writing and lobbying to demonstrations and marches to peaceful civil disobedience at Trident bases. Action is always sustained by a strong base of prayer and meditation and draws inspiration from the spiritually based non-violent movements of Gandhi, Martin Luther King and the anti-apartheid movement in South Africa. The principle and practice of non-violence is of great importance to the Iona Community.

Women in Black is a worldwide peace network of women who bear witness against the cruelties of war. They stand in silent vigil in public places to protest against war, rape as a tool of war, ethnic cleansing and human rights abuses all over the world. Their silence is visible. They invite other women to stand with them, and to reflect on their lives and on women who have been raped, tortured or killed in concentration camps; women who have disappeared, or whose loved ones have disappeared; women who have been killed and their homes demolished … They wear black as a symbol of sorrow for all the victims of war, for the destruction of people, nature and the fabric of life.

Women in Black vigils were started in Israel in 1988 by women protesting against Israel's occupation of the West Bank and Gaza. The movement has developed in a number of European countries, notably in former Yugoslavia where women have stood in weekly vigils since 1991 to protest against war and the Serbian regime's policies of nationalist aggression. Groups have formed in many US cities since September 11th, 2001. Many Iona Community members are also part of Women in Black in Scotland.

The Justice and Peace Commitment of the Iona Community

Peacemaking and opposition to militarisation has been a central part of the Iona Community's life since its beginning in 1938. After having been awarded the Military Cross in the trenches of the First World War, George MacLeod, the community's founder, became a convert to radical non-violence and to sustained, costly opposition to militarisation, nuclear weapons and the arms trade. This commitment to non-violence shaped the Iona Community in many ways and resulted in the adoption by the community of the Peace and Justice Commitment – one part of the five-fold Rule of faith and life to which all members adhere. The Peace and Justice Commitment was adopted unanimously in 1966 and is only changed by the consent of all the members.

The Justice and Peace Commitment

We believe:

1. that the gospel commands us to seek peace founded on justice and that costly reconciliation is at the heart of the gospel;

2. that work for justice, peace and an equitable society is a matter of extreme urgency;

3. that God has given us partnership as stewards of creation and that we have a responsibility to live in a right relationship with the whole of

God's creation;

4. that, handled with integrity, creation can provide for the needs of all, but not for the greed which leads to injustice and inequality, and endangers life on earth;

5. that everyone should have the quality and dignity of a full life that requires adequate physical, social and political opportunity, without the oppression of poverty, injustice and fear;

6. that social and political action leading to justice for all people and encouraged by prayer and discussion is a vital work of the Church at all levels;

7. that the use or threatened use of nuclear and other weapons of mass destruction is theologically and morally indefensible and that opposition to their existence is an imperative of the Christian faith.

As members and family groups we will:

8. engage in forms of political witness and action, prayerfully and thoughtfully, to promote just and peaceful social, political and economic structures;

9. work for a policy of renunciation by our own nations of all weapons of mass destruction, and for the encouragement of other nations, individually or collectively, to do the same;

10. celebrate human diversity and actively work to combat discrimination on grounds of age, colour, disability, mental well-being, differing ability, gender, colour, race, ethnic and cultural background, sexual orientation or religion;

11. work for the establishment of the United Nations Organisation as the principal organ of international reconciliation and security, in place of military alliances;

12. support and promote research and education into non-violent ways of achieving justice, peace and a sustainable global society;

13. work for reconciliation within and among nations by international sharing and exchange of experience and people, with particular concern for politically and economically oppressed nations.

Although we are inadequate and fail constantly, these ideals are, nevertheless, what we seek to live by. They draw their inspiration, partly at least, from the witness of Adomnán.

Violence against women today

The *Law of the Innocents* was primarily a law to protect women from violence in time of war. We should not be in any doubt that violence against women remains a major form of oppression worldwide.

- In Scotland, it is estimated that 40,000 women in Glasgow alone live in intimate relationships which include regular physical, sexual and emotional abuse.

- In the USA, a woman is beaten every fifteen seconds; a woman is raped every six minutes; every day, four women are killed by abusive men.

- In parts of Africa, thousands of female children are routinely subjected to genital mutilation.

- There is a large-scale global industry in the trafficking of women.

- Sex tourism exploits and ruins the lives of countless girls and boys.

- Rape is a war crime used on a massive scale in Korea, Bosnia, Rwanda, the Gulf and other fields of conflict.

- In Mexico, 95% of women claim sexual harassment at work.

- It is estimated that at least one in three female children, and an uncalculated number of male children, suffer some form of sexual abuse, usually at the hands of a known man.

- 85% of rapists are known to their victims and 60% of rapes are committed indoors – mostly in the woman's own home.[1]

Violence against women is endemic around the globe. The British Medical Association has named it as a major health hazard in this country. Police estimate that 1 in 4 women will experience violence against them in their lifetimes (about 90% of all abuse is by men against women). And just as was the case in the horrific battlefield story found in the *Cáin Adomnáin,* violence against women ultimately cannot be separated from violence against children. Women who suffer abuse are often – as in the Old Testament, and still in many parts of the world – actually of an age we would consider to be within childhood. Violence against a woman has a hugely damaging effect on her children and often includes or leads to child abuse. And the fear of what will happen to their children makes women more vulnerable to threat.

Twenty years ago it was still quite legal for a man to rape his wife. Not any more. Gradually the law is beginning to reflect in practice what it previously only reflected in theory: that women and children, not just men, have the fullness of humanity and are entitled in their own right to protection and equal treatment under the law. It is extremely encouraging that the Scottish Parliament made domestic violence a priority for response in its first term. We are moving nearer to a time when the law may actually be used to deliver justice rather than guard the interests of the powerful. The *Law of the Innocents* has been a part of this long and very slow process.

The complicity of the Church

As a Christian community, we know too that there are some aspects of traditional Christian practice and teaching which have seemed to legitimise violence against women. In various books of the Old Testament, women are sexually assaulted, raped by strangers, raped by their brothers and other male relatives, gang raped to death, and offered for sex by their male relatives. Women are used as sexual shields and decoys by their husbands; abducted, kidnapped and married against their will; sold into slavery, concubinage and prostitution by male relatives. They are forced to act as surrogate mothers. And they are beaten, humiliated and killed by abandonment, starvation, violence and acts of war.

In the New Testament, women are commanded, with all the authority that male church leaders can muster, to obey their husbands, to submit to male authority and to keep silent. Of course, this is not a very subtle or nuanced description of what the New Testament has to say about the relationship between men and women. But then, the uses to which Paul's teaching, for example, have been put have not been very subtle or nuanced either. If someone wishes to use scripture, tradition and centuries of Church history to justify the subordination and submission of women to men, and hence his right to beat or sexually abuse his partner, he is likely to slide over a passage such as this one from Ephesians: 'No more shouting or insults, no more hateful feelings of any sort, instead, be kind and tender-hearted to one another.' (4:32)

It must be said, of course, that no religion has a monopoly on taking it upon itself to offer divine authorisation for violence against women. Recently there has been outrage among women's groups in Turkey because a religious leader there has written a book advising men on the correct way to beat their wives – so that it doesn't show. And we are all aware now of what life under the Taliban was like for women. Nor for Christians is this a matter of merely historical concern. Men who abuse women still routinely call upon the Bible as their authority and justification in every Christian country in the world, including Scotland.

We are living with a terrible legacy of extreme and persistent violence against women and a sorry history in which the Church has routinely denied, ignored, covered up and protected abusers. For breaking the silence alone, Adomnán deserves our recognition. For, as Monica Furlong wrote somewhat acerbically: 'If … we had to wait for the churches to promote tertiary education for women, the Married Woman's Property Act, the franchise, entry to the professions, equal pay for equal work, the Sex Discrimination Act, and many other measures vital to women's health and well-being, we should still be waiting. Indeed the churches frequently opposed such reforms.'

In Celtic Ireland, as in many other ages and places, 'protection of women' was bought at the cost of indebtedness and obedience to male hierarchy, economic and spiritual power and definitions of proper female behaviour. In our own time and context, perhaps we can ring our 'wee true-judging bells' to break that dependence so that women, and others who suffer violence, may find their own power of resistance. This is the hope of those in the Iona Community who belong to Women in Black, and who work in the churches to ensure that gender violence is no longer accepted and covered up.

Protection of non-combatants and the 'just war' theory

The *Cáin Adomnáin* was for the protection of non-combatants. The treatise is not itself a non-violent document. It fights fire with fire, uses extremely violent threats and includes execution and amputation in its list of punishments. It is of its time and context and should be judged thus; therefore it is wonderful that one of its most significant tenets is about complicity:

'But he who from this day forward shall put a woman to death and does not do penance according to the Law, shall not only perish in eternity, and be cursed for God and Adomnán, but all shall be cursed that have heard it and do not curse him and do not chastise him according to the judgement of this Law.'

It is not enough for good men to do nothing. Silence, as Nadezhda Mandelstam said from the gulags, is also a crime.

The *Cáin Adomnáin* drew a clear line of differentiation between combatants and those we would now describe as civilians. That differentiation was important for other teachers and theologians of the Church, from St Augustine of Hippo to St Thomas Aquinas, who attempted to legislate for, and limit, the horror and cruelty of war. Early Christian apologists were absolute pacifists; and conversion to Christianity for another saint important on Iona, St Martin of Tours – often described as the father of Celtic monasticism – meant abandoning his military profession for the practice of non-violence. 'I am a soldier of Christ; I cannot fight,' he said. In formulating and developing the theory of the 'just war', these interpreters shaped what was accepted by the twentieth century as conditions under which a war could be fought:

- The war must be defensive and a response to unjust aggression.
- All other methods of resolving the conflict must have been exhausted.

- There must be a realistic chance of success to justify all the wartime sacrifices.
- There must be some proportion between the moral and physical costs of the hostilities and the peace and better social order sought afterwards.
- Only military installations, not unarmed civilians, can be the targets of military strikes.
- Force may never be used as a means in itself or to brutalise the social order and the military personnel.

It is the belief of the Iona Community, expressed in our Justice and Peace Commitment, that there are no circumstances in which the use of Trident would conform to all or even most of these conditions. The twentieth century saw the proportions of civilian to military casualties grow inversely, so that in all the wars fought recently, and still being fought, civilian casualties outnumbered military ones hugely. This would be particularly the case with Trident and is one of the reasons that the Iona Community, aligning itself with Adomnán's Law protecting the innocents, has a fifty-year history of active opposition to nuclear weapons.

But beyond that, and because we are committed not just to the protection of innocents but to the belief that unjust and violent means do not bring about just and peaceful outcomes, we work through non-violence at every level for changes in the *culture* of violence. The current situation where our country is engaged in prosecuting a war begs so many questions in relation to the just war theory that it is possible to conclude that a serious confusion has arisen between a just *cause* and a just *war*. The first may not be in doubt. The conviction of just cause elicits the 'we can't just do nothing' response. It's too late to ponder whether, as is often the case, it's better to do nothing than to do the wrong thing. The stakes have been hugely raised, and now the breakdown of international trust and goodwill, and the survival of the UN, must be factored into the overall equation. The notion of the just war may have some utility when getting *into* a war (few countries will voluntarily surrender the moral high ground) but it has much less use in getting out of it. War itself is brutalising; even its language dehumanises, as the evidence from Guantanamo Bay and Abu Ghraib has demonstrated so starkly. This is especially the case when there are numerous factions involved in the post-war dispensation, each with its own claim to legitimacy and different maps for the same territory. Such intractable conflicts have proved acutely resistant to imposed solutions from elsewhere.

By selecting this particular 'just cause' out of so many in the world, and by electing to insert themselves into the cycle of violence in Iraq at this particular point in history, will the US and Britain have helped to shift events any nearer to a just and peaceful future? Or are we just a new part of the problem? If we are, what will it take to become part of the solution?

Adomnán, under severe pressure from his mother it must be said, chose against all the odds, and in the face of a fierce culture of violence, to become part of the solution. In a world in which the innocents are exposed and suffer in unprecedented numbers, perhaps the best recognition and tribute we can pay to his efforts is to try to become part of the solution in our time.

Kathy Galloway

Note:

1. These statistics are from various sources, including Zero Tolerance Campaign material and the international conference held in Brighton in 1996: 'Violence, Abuse and Women's Citizenship'. Statistics cited in the essay 'Nightmares in the Garden: Christianity and sexual violence', Lesley Macdonald, in *Dreaming of Eden: Reflections on Christianity and Sexuality*, Kathy Galloway, Wild Goose Publications, 1997.

APPENDIX C:

An Adomnán Liturgy of Celebration

AN ADOMNÁN LITURGY OF CELEBRATION

To mark 'Carnival' at Faslane (Trident nuclear missile submarine base),
13 May 2000

St Adomnán of Iona is best known as the biographer of St Columba. However, in his own time he was recognised as the author of the *Cáin Adomnáin*, or *Law of the Innocents*. Known as 'the first law in heaven and earth for the protection of women', Adomnán's Law extended to children and clergy, and is an early attempt to protect non-combatants. It is a precursor of the Geneva Conventions and the United Nations' Declaration of Human Rights. It was said that instead of carrying a sword into battle, Adomnán carried a bell, 'the bell of Adomnán's anger', which he rang out against injustice and the tyrants of his day.[1]

Part one: A time for diagnosis

Leader 1:   Now is the time to live, to come to the Creator, to sing and dance to the Lord who frees us from fear, to help create a better world with the Spirit of Love. (*Bell rings once*)

(*Short silence*)

Leader 1:   Let us invite the whole world to join us in praise.
All: The time has come. (*Bell*)

Leader 2:   Let us acknowledge our failures to live as God's children.
All: The time has come. (*Bell*)

Leader 3:   For our willingness to use Trident, we seek God's pardon.
All: The time has come. (*Bell*)

Leader 4:   For our failure to amend our lives and share with others the fruits of creation, we ask God's pardon.

All: The time has come. *(Bell)*

Leader 1:   For our reluctance as a society to acknowledge our sickness and accept healing, we ask God's pardon.

All: The time has come. *(Bell)*

(Short silence)

Leader 2:   Many times we have come to this place and seen the horror it inflicts on our land. We know what worse horrors it could inflict on other people's lands, on our God-given planet, should the weaponry deployed here ever be used. We have often used both Scripture and Adomnán's Law to remind those who work here of their responsibility, and ours, to both God and humanity. Today we come to remind ourselves, as well as those who work here, of our responsibility to heal the sickness of our society, to heal this place and restore Faslane Bay again to a health spa, a place of celebration. We hear again Ezekiel, but listen to the message of responsibility to celebrate life.

Reader: (Reading from the Prophet Ezekiel, Chapter 37:1–14)

(Short silence)

Part two: A time for healing

Leader 2:   We seek to heal this place of Death

All: Deep peace to you *(Bell)*

Leader 3:   We seek to heal all those who work here from the sickness of fear
All: Deep peace to you *(Bell)*

Leader 4:   We seek to heal the world's hunger by redistributing resources
All: Deep peace to you *(Bell)*

Leader 1:   We seek to heal the environment of all that harms life
All: Deep peace to you *(Bell)*

Leader 2:   We seek to heal and make whole all who would hold life truly a gift from God
All: Deep peace to you *(Bell)*

(Short silence)

Leader 3:   We have often rung the Bell of Adomnán in this place as a symbolic reminder of that law honoured by our Celtic ancestors and by those who walked in the traditions of Iona. That Bell often was known as a sign of condemnation of those who failed to keep the law. It is also the case, however, that in Celtic tradition, bells, and particularly Adomnán's Bell, were often used as a sign of healing. We invite you now to ring your own small bells, as Adomnán's heirs, as a symbol of your will to bring healing on this place and on all who are present today.

(Time for lots of bells to be rung.)

Part three: A time for celebration

Leader 4:   Most religious traditions stress the importance of sharing. Many also see the deep value of sharing a meal. In the simple act of partaking of the same gifts of the earth, people are bound together in a common act of humanity, a sacred trust. As we come to this place, we are witnesses to the imbalance of our sharing of the earth's resources. In the tradition of the Christian community of Columba and Adomnán, we hear again of a great symbolic act of sharing.

Reader: *(Reading from the Gospel of Mark 6:30–44)*

Leader 1:   We may not be able to feed five thousand here today. But we invite you to share symbolically in what we have. These gifts are already an act of trust, an act of sharing. Since Trident Ploughshares 2000 got under way, some of the Adomnán of Iona Affinity Group have been visited regularly by the Lothian and Borders CID (Criminal Investigation Department). On each occasion we have shared hospitality with them. On the last two visits, they kindly brought provisions for our 'working afternoon tea'. We could not consume all the fragments of the last session, and, as they themselves said, 'There is enough to share with your friends.' We now invite you to share in their gift to us all. A gift of friendship. A gift of mutual trust and respect. A gift of a pledge of a fully healed future.

(We share biscuits and juice with, firstly, any police, then each other and any of the folk who are around us.)

Conclusion: Litany of celebration
(with acknowledgement to Norman C. Habel [2])

Leader 1:   Today the Lord steps into the air once more, to taste its colour and feel its songs. He inhales the thoughts of children, the hopes of yesterday, the fantasies of tomorrow, and he wonders whether his children are too old to celebrate their dreams.

All: Let us spin him our dreams.

Leader 2:   Someday soon people here will celebrate life every day.

All: We would do it now.

Leader 3:   Someday soon people will turn this place into a holiday camp.

All: Turn the Ship Lift into a cafeteria.

Leader 4:   Someday soon people will glimpse the face of God in each other.

All: Use the eyes of friends in place of mirrors.

Leader 5:   Someday soon people will sink their teeth into politics for peace.

All: Share their food with the hungry.

Leader 1:   Someday soon people will turn all bombs into beachballs.

All: All Trident missiles into railway trains.

Leader 2:   Someday soon people will slow down and wait for God.

All: Run and dance through Faslane base with bare feet.

Leader 3:   Someday soon people will laugh in the restored spring grass.

All: Dance in the nuclear-free waves.

Leader 4:   Someday soon people will celebrate Easter every day.

All: And hang Christmas banners from the moon.

Leader 5:   Someday soon people will live like that.

All: But we plan to start right now! Amen! Right now!

(We share our balloons with everybody, draw on them etc., but slowly move off to our chosen place to continue the 'party'.)

Notes on the service:

At some point in the Office – we are very flexible – we read or proclaim part of the *Cáin Adomnáin* or *Adomnán's Law*, paragraphs 28, 27, 33, 34 and sometimes part of 35. We conclude with section 21 in full. We generally give a short introduction to its date and significance in its own time. We then try to add to that its relevance for us as Iona Community members or 'Heirs of Adomnán'. Depending on which bells we have, they are rung either at this point or during the action itself. For the opening of the campaign back in August 1998, we had large pictures of victims of Hiroshima lined up across the gate. We had been lent the Abbey copy of the Adomnán Bell – a gift of the Corrymeela Community. We managed to create a silence and then stood in front of each portrait and simply rang the bell for each one. It was very moving. Just for the record, after the litany of celebration, the 'party' continued until members of the Adomnán Group and others were arrested.

The Adomnán Affinity Group (Maire-Colette Wilkie)

Notes:

1. Introduction drawn (by Neil Paynter) from *Cáin Adomnáin (Adomnán's Law), a seventh-century law for the protection of non-combatants*, translated with an introduction by Gilbert Márkus, Blackfriars Books, Glasgow, 1997

2. The 'litany of celebration' is adapted from 'Dreams of celebration', © Norman C. Habel from his book *Interrobang* (Lutterworth Press, 1970)

BOOKS AND ARTICLES FOR FURTHER READING

Adomnán at Birr, AD 697: Essays in commemoration of the Law of the Innocents, T. O'Loughlin, Four Courts Press, 2001

Adomnán's Law of the Innocents, G. Márkus, Blackfriars Books, Glasgow, 1997

'Adomnán's Law for women, clerics and youths, 697', M. Ní Dhonnchadha, in *Chattel, Servant or Citizen: Women's status in Church, state and society*, edited by M. O'Dowd and S. Wichert, Institute of Irish Studies, Belfast, 1995

'Bede, Adomnán and the writing of history', J.M. Picard, *Peritia 3: Journal of the Medieval Academy of Ireland*, 1984, pp.50–70

Celtic Theology: Humanity, World and God in early Irish writings, T. O'Loughlin, Continuum, 2000

Ecclesiastical History of the English People, Bede; edited and translated by B. Colgrave and R.A.B. Mynors, Oxford University Press, 1969

Iona, Kells and Derry, M. Herbert, Four Courts Press, Dublin, 1996

Iona, Tara and Soissons: The origins of the royal anointing ritual in Francia, M.J. Enright, published by Walter de Gruyter, 1985

Iona: The Earliest Poetry of a Celtic Monastery, T.O. Clancy and G. Márkus, Edinburgh University Press, 1995

Ireland and her Neighbours in the Seventh Century, M. Richter, Four Courts Press, 1999

Life of St Columba, Adomnán, translation and introduction by R. Sharpe, Penguin, 1995

The Age of Bede, translated by J.F. Webb, edited by D.H. Farmer, Penguin, 2004

The Convention of Drum Cett, J. Bannerman, Scottish Gaelic Studies, 11:1, 1966, pp.114–129

'The guarantor list of Cáin Adomnáin', M. Ní Dhonnchadha, *Peritia 1: Journal of the Medieval Academy of Ireland,* 1982, pp.178–215

Warlords and Holy Men, A.P. Smyth, Edinburgh University Press, 1989

SOURCES

'I have loved the land of Ireland – I cry for parting ...' – from *The Poem Book of the Gael: Translations from Irish Gaelic poetry into English prose and verse*, edited and translated by Eleanor Hull, Chatto and Windus, 1912

'He suffered briefly until he triumphed ...' – from Amra Choluimb Chille (7th century) – by Dallán Forgaill, from *Iona: The Earliest Poetry of a Celtic Monastery*, Thomas Owen Clancy and Gilbert Márkus, Edinburgh University Press, 1995, ISBN 0748605312. Used by permission of Edinburgh University Press.

Luke 21:10–11, 28 – *Revised English Bible* © Oxford University Press and Cambridge University Press 1989. Used with permission.

'He was a wise and worthy man ...' – from Bede: *Ecclesiastical History of the English People*, p.294. 'The history' translated by Leo Sherley-Price and revised by R.E. Latham, translation of the minor works, new Introduction and Notes by D.H. Farmer (Penguin Classics 1955, Revised edition 1968, 1990). Translation copyright Leo Sherley-Price, 1955, 1968. Used by permission of Penguin Group (UK)

Matthew 13:52 – *Revised English Bible* © Oxford University Press and Cambridge University Press 1989. Used with permission.

Esther 4:14 – *Revised Standard Version of the Bible*, copyright 1952 (2nd edition, 1971) by the Division of Christian Education of the National Council of the Churches of Christ in the United States of America. Used by permission. All rights reserved

'Three labours in the day ...' – From the Rule of Columcille, translator unknown. From the appendix of *Lays of Iona and Other Poems*, S. Stone, Longmans, Green & Co., 1897, p.112

'That I might bless the Lord ...' – from *The Poem Book of the Gael: Translations from Irish Gaelic poetry into English prose and verse,* edited and translated by Eleanor Hull, Chatto and Windus, 1912, p.237

Leviticus 11:44 – *Revised English Bible* © Oxford University Press and Cambridge University Press 1989. Used with permission.

Quote from John Wesley – from *Scriptural Christianity: Forty-four sermons by John Wesley,* Epworth Press, 1944.

Psalm 137:4 – *Revised English Bible* © Oxford University Press and Cambridge University Press 1989. Used with permission.

'I huddle insensible as blank air ...' – from *An Evil Cradling* by Brian Keenan, published by Hutchinson. Reprinted by permission of the The Random House Group Ltd and Elaine Steel.

'Although he was their lawfully constituted head ...' – from Bede: *Ecclesiastical History of the English People,* p.320. 'The history' translated by Leo Sherley-Price and revised by R.E. Latham, translation of the minor works, new Introduction and Notes by D.H. Farmer (Penguin Classics 1955, Revised edition 1968, 1990). Translation copyright Leo Sherley-Price, 1955, 1968. Used by permission of Penguin Group (UK)

'Tired and lonely ...' – From *Markings* by Dag Hammarskjöld, translated by W.H. Auden & Leif Sjoberg, copyright © 1964 by Alfred A. Knopf, a division of Random House, Inc. and Faber & Faber Ltd. Used by permission of Alfred A. Knopf, a division of Random House, Inc and Faber & Faber Ltd.

'To Adomnán of Iona, whose troop is radiant ...' from *Martyrology of Oengus,* c.830, quoted in *Adomnán's Law of the Innocents,* G. Márkus, Blackfriars Books, Glasgow, 1997

The Lex Innocentium ...' – Thomas Owen Clancy, from *Hope of Scots*, edited by Dauvit Broun and Thomas Owen Clancy, T&T Clark, 1999. Used by permission of Continuum.

'Adomnán at Birr ...' – Thomas O'Loughlin, from *Celtic Theology*, Thomas O'Loughlin, Continuum, 2000, p.70. Quoted in Adomnán *at Birr, AD 697: Essays in commemoration of the Law of the Innocents*, Thomas O'Loughlin, Four Courts Press, Dublin 2001. Used by permission of Continuum.

'He was an angel in demeanour, blameless in what he said, godly in what he did ...' – From *Life of St Columba* by Adomnán of Iona, translated by Richard Sharpe (Penguin Classics, 1995). Copyright © Richard Sharpe, 1995. Used by permission of Penguin Group (UK)

'Do not go gentle ...' – excerpt from 'Do Not go Gentle Into That Good Night' from *The Poems of Dylan Thomas*, copyright © 1952 by Dylan Thomas. Reprinted by permission of New Directions Publishing Corp and David Higham Associates Ltd.

'I have written down these things ...' – Adomnán, *De Locis Sanctis,* edited and translated by D. Meehan & L. Bieler, *Scriptores Latini Hiberniae 3*, Dublin 1958

An Adomnán liturgy of celebration – by the Adomnán Affinity Group (Maire-Colette Wilkie), from *This is The Day: Readings and Meditations from the Iona Community*, Neil Paynter (ed), Wild Goose Publications, 2002. Used by permission of Maire-Colette Wilkie and Wild Goose Publications. www.ionabooks.com

PHOTOGRAPHS:

David Coleman – p.23, p.49, p.59, p.69, p.126, p.159

Jon Crosby – cover photo, boat

Katrina Crosby – p.51. p.91

Margaret Hogan – p.118 (Birr Old Church, near the site of St Brendan's monastery)

Photographs © the photographers

THE IONA COMMUNITY IS:

- An ecumenical movement of men and women from different walks of life and different traditions in the Christian church
- Committed to the gospel of Jesus Christ, and to following where that leads, even into the unknown
- Engaged together, and with people of goodwill across the world, in acting, reflecting and praying for justice, peace and the integrity of creation
- Convinced that the inclusive community we seek must be embodied in the community we practise

Together with our staff, we are responsible for:

- Our islands residential centres of Iona Abbey, the MacLeod Centre on Iona, and Camas Adventure Centre on the Ross of Mull

and in Glasgow:

- The administration of the Community
- Our work with young people
- Our publishing house, Wild Goose Publications
- Our association in the revitalising of worship with the Wild Goose Resource Group

The Iona Community was founded in Glasgow in 1938 by George MacLeod, minister, visionary and prophetic witness for peace, in the context of the poverty and despair of the Depression. Its original task of rebuilding the monastic ruins of Iona Abbey became a sign of hopeful rebuilding of community in Scotland and beyond. Today, we are about 250 Members, mostly in Britain, and 1500 Associate Members, with 1400 Friends worldwide. Together and apart, 'we follow the light we have, and pray for more light'.

For information on the Iona Community contact:
The Iona Community, Fourth Floor, Savoy House, 140 Sauchiehall Street,
Glasgow G2 3DH, UK. Phone: 0141 332 6343
e-mail: ionacomm@gla.iona.org.uk; web: www.iona.org.uk

For enquiries about visiting Iona, please contact:
Iona Abbey, Isle of Iona, Argyll PA76 6SN, UK. Phone: 01681 700404
e-mail: ionacomm@iona.org.uk

Wild Goose Publications, the publishing house of the Iona Community established in the Celtic Christian tradition of Saint Columba, produces books, tapes and CDs on:

- holistic spirituality
- social justice
- political and peace issues
- healing
- innovative approaches to worship
- song in worship, including the work of the Wild Goose Resource Group
- material for meditation and reflection

If you would like to find out more about our books, tapes and CDs, please contact us at:

Wild Goose Publications
Fourth Floor, Savoy House
140 Sauchiehall Street,
Glasgow G2 3DH, UK

Tel. +44 (0)141 332 6292
Fax +44 (0)141 332 1090
e-mail: admin@ionabooks.com

or visit our website at
www.ionabooks.com
for details of all our products and online sales